Self-Discovery Journal

to Accompany

Contemporary Psychology and Effective Behavior

Seventh Edition

Charles G. Morris
The University of Michigan

HarperCollins*Publishers*

Acknowledgments

pp. 15–16   Excerpt from "Aggression-Altruism: A Scale and Some data on its Reliability and Validity" by Knud Larsen from *Journal of Personality Assessment,* vol. 35, pp. 275-81, 1971. Reprinted by permission.

pp. 26–27   From "A Study of Same Sex Touching Attitudes: Scale Development and Personality Predictors" by Knud S. Larsen and Jeff LeRoux from *The Journal of Sex Research,* vol. 20, no. 3, August, 1984. Reprinted by permission.

pp. 48–50   Excerpts reprinted with permission of the publisher from: Larsen, K.S., Klar, L.R., Rex, G., & White, C. "Attitudes toward death: a desensitization hypothesis." *Psychological Reports,* 1974, 35, 687-90.

pp. 57–58   Excerpts reprinted with permission of the publisher from: Martin, N.J., & Larsen, K.S. "Measurement of competitive-cooperative attitudes." *Psychological Reports,* 1976, 39, 303-06.

pp. 72–74   Excerpts from "Attitudes of Heterosexuals Toward Homosexuality: A Likert-Type Scale and Construct Validity" by Knud S. Larsen, Michael Reed and Susan Hoffman from *The Journal of Sex Research,* vol. 16, no. 3, August, 1980. Reprinted by permission.

ISBN 0-673-47940-4

3   4   5   6-RRD-94   93   92   91

Preface

The essays and exercises in this *Self-Discovery Journal* are meant to serve two purposes. First, they will help you understand the ways in which the issues discussed in *CPEB* apply to your own life. A course in adjustment psychology is, at least in part, based on theory. The exercises in this journal will let you see how that theory relates in your life and in those of others around you. For instance, in Chapter 3 you will read about a number of things that can cause stress. The materials in Chapter 3 of this journal will enable you to explore those things that are particularly stressful for you and to learn how you react to stress, sometimes before you are even conscious that you are having any problems.

The second purpose of the chapters of this journal is even more personal. Here you can keep a "running diary" of things that you have learned about yourself during the course of this semester. For instance, all of us know people that we liked (or did not like) from the very first minute we saw them. For the most part we simply accept our responses, but some of the exercises in Chapter 10 provide ways for you to analyze at least some of the reasons for such a reaction. The hope is that you will become more and more acquainted with your own unique self, for without that knowledge, many of the adjustive tasks you will face in your lifetime may be far more difficult than they need be.

Each chapter of the *Self-Discovery Journal* is divided into three parts: *Activities, Surveying Your Perspectives,* and *Explorations.* The first, *Activities,* presents fairly structured projects, some of which will require you to work with at least one other classmate. For instance, you will be asked to interview someone who works at a crisis center or is either a formal or informal counselor. Or you will be asked to react to an article about relaxation techniques in a psychology journal or to record your observations after an afternoon of watching children play at a schoolyard or park.

Surveying Your Perspectives, which are less structured than *Activities,* are much like interest inventories. Often you will be asked to rank statements on a sliding scale. These exercises will help you focus your attention upon your own beliefs and values, some of which many people are unaware until they are encouraged to work through a structured questionnaire like the ones in these sections.

Both *Activities* and *Surveying Your Perspectives* are designed to prepare you for the *Exploration* section that ends every chapter in the journal. Far less structured than the earlier sections, most ask you to write short paragraphs that will help you explore your own beliefs, attitudes and values. For instance, in Part II, which discusses stress and stress management, you can analyze particularly stressful events by assessing your reactions, considering ways in which you might have coped more effectively with the stressor, and identifying early warning signs that you are reaching the limits of your ability to cope without professional assistance. Other chapters enable you to examine such things as your beliefs and values and how they affect your choice of friends, loved ones, and career goals.

All in all, even though this *Self-Discovery Journal* is a learning tool designed to help you understand the concepts that are integral to this course and to *CPEB*, the journal is also your own private tool, a way to discover the concepts that are integral to your own character. We urge you to write down your answers as you go along; this book can then serve as a permanent record of your thoughts about yourself and your world. Referring back to these thoughts in future years, sharing them with those closest to you, and adding to them from time to time as your ideas change can be an extraordinarily interesting and worthwhile experience.

Contents

PART ONE ADJUSTMENT AND THE INDIVIDUAL

Chapter 1   The Human Dilemma   1
Chapter 2   The Quest for Understanding   8

PART TWO STRESS: ITS NATURE, EFFECTS, AND MANAGEMENT

Chapter 3   Problems of Adjustment   13
Chapter 4   Reactions to Stressful Events   19
Chapter 5   Effective Methods of Coping with Stress   23
Chapter 6   Maladaptive Behavior   31
Chapter 7   Psychotherapy and Counseling   37

PART THREE ADJUSTING TO CHALLENGES OVER A LIFETIME

Chapter 8   Development and Adjustment in Childhood and Adolescence   42
Chapter 9   Development and Adjustment in Adulthood   47

PART FOUR INTERPERSONAL AND SOCIAL ASPECTS OF ADJUSTMENT

Chapter 10   Interpersonal Patterns and Relationships   54
Chapter 11   Love, Marriage, and Intimacy   63
Chapter 12   Sexual Attitudes and Behavior   71
Chapter 13   Work and Leisure   77
Chapter 14   Adjusting to Living in Groups   83

EPILOGUE THE QUEST FOR VALUES   86

The Human Dilemma

1. Review television programming for one day: (a) List all topics covered; (b) Total number of hours of potential T.V. choice; and (c) How you made your choice. If your class is divided into small groups, discuss the factors which determined (a) Whether you watched television at a given hour; (b) How you went about deciding which programs to see from the many choices; (c) What attitudes affected your program decisions.

All Topics Covered (List)	Number of Hours	How Choice Was Made

2. Is your adjustive behavior effective? For one week keep track of alcohol, tranquilizer, and sleeping pill usage.

Amount Consumed			
	Alcohol	Tranquilizers	Sleeping Pills
Monday			
Tuesday			
Wednesday			
Thursday			
Friday			
Saturday			
Sunday			

Do you have a problem with stress as indicated by your usage pattern? What factors contribute to these problems? Identify.

3. Examine a current newspaper. Count the number of articles which deal with the past, the present, and the future. What time dimension is our primary focus?

	Past		Present		Future
Article	Topic	Article	Topic	Article	Topic

Total articles	

Surveying Your Perspective

Ladder Device	Self-anchoring Scale	Step Number
10	Picture a ladder. Suppose we say that the top of the ladder represents the best possible life for you and the bottom represents the worst possible life for you.	
9		
8	After each question, just write the place on the ladder you think is appropriate for you *now*. Don't be hesitant or embarrassed in putting yourself near the top or near the bottom of the ladder *if* that is the way you happen to feel. Just give your first reaction without thinking too much about it.	
7		
6		
5		
4	Where on the ladder do you feel you personally stand at the *present* time?	_____
3	Where on the ladder would you say you stood *five years ago?*	_____
2		
1	And where do you think you will be on the ladder *five years from now?*	_____

To what extent do you feel there is a good deal you can do *yourself* to make your life happier and more satisfying than it is, as contrasted to the feeling that there isn't very much you can do about it yourself. Let the top of the ladder stand for being able to do a good deal for yourself, the bottom stand for a feeling of rather complete helplessness.

____

Now, how about the extent to which you feel you have an opportunity to do what you would like to do, as contrasted to the feeling that you are doing only what you have "got" to do. Think of the top of the ladder as being completely free to do what you want to do, the bottom as doing what you have to do.

____

How would you rate yourself as to how successful or unsuccessful you have been in terms of achieving your own goals and aims in life? Think of the top of the ladder as being completely successful, the bottom as being entirely unsuccessful.

____

To what extent do you feel life is full of troubles or obstacles? This time think of the *top* of the ladder as indicating a person whose life is mainly a whole series of problems and obstacles he is facing and the *bottom* as a person without troubles or obstacles.

____

This is a modification of the Cantril Self-Anchoring Striving Scale. The majority of people's hopes and fears revolve essentially around *personal* well-being. These are often defined as a decent standard of living; opportunities for children; technological advances; good health; a good job; decent housing; a happy home life; better educational facilties; ". . . concern for greater social justice, more freedom, better moral standards, the resolution of moral and ethical problems and similar goals appears to be the conscious concern of only a tiny minority of people throughout the world." (p. 146)

References

Cantril, H. (1967). *The human dimension: Experiences in policy research.* New Brunswick, NJ: Rutgers University Press.
Simmons, D. Oregon State University, 1986.

We have seen that human beings have a unique capacity for self-direction, and that this places a heavy demand upon each of us to try to find answers to the three key questions: "Who am I?" "Where am I going?" and "How do I get there?" The material on the next several pages will help you begin to develop your own answers to these key questions. In subsequent chapters we will build on your answers here and, in the process, help you move toward a more complete and comprehensive understanding of yourself and the world around you.

Who Am I?

A. Before you read any further, stop for a few minutes and think: if you were to describe your personality to someone else using just ten adjectives, what adjectives would you use? What kind of person are you? Write those ten adjectives in the space below:

B. Now look at the following list of adjectives, some of which may apply to you and some of which may not. In the space in front of each adjective, write a number to indicate how well that adjective describes you. Use the following scale:

4—Very true of me; this adjective describes me very well.

3—Somewhat true of me; I usually tend to be this way.

2—Not very true of me; I am seldom this way.

1—Not at all true of me; this adjective doesn't describe me at all.

_____ 1. adventurous

_____ 2. cooperative

_____ 3. frivolous

_____ 4. high-strung

_____ 5. well-read

_____ 6. shy

_____ 7. calm

_____ 8. spiteful

_____ 9. persevering

_____ 10. unimaginative

_____ 11. undependable

_____ 12. talkative

_____ 13. clumsy

_____ 14. stable

_____ 15. irritable

_____ 16. methodical

_____ 17. reserved

_____ 18. intellectual

_____ 19. emotional

_____ 20. agreeable

_____ 21. careless

_____ 22. unshakable

_____ 23. self-revealing

_____ 24. inquiring

_____ 25. touchy

_____ 26. quiet

_____ 27. narrow

_____ 28. conscientious

_____ 29. demanding	_____ 35. coarse	_____ 41. energetic	_____ 46. soft-hearted
_____ 30. good-natured	_____ 36. retiring	_____ 42. irresponsible	_____ 47. withdrawn
_____ 31. confident	_____ 37. considerate	_____ 43. realistic	_____ 48. orderly
_____ 32. sociable	_____ 38. unpredictable	_____ 44. critical	_____ 49. insecure
_____ 33. stubborn	_____ 39. worrying	_____ 45. cultured	_____ 50. naive
_____ 34. responsible	_____ 40. refined		

C. Now look back over the adjectives that you rated 3 or 4. Those are the adjectives that are most descriptive of you. People differ somewhat in the personal characteristics that they consider to be desirable or undesirable, positive or negative. Based on your own opinions about desirable and undesirable characteristics, are the adjectives you rated 3 or 4 mostly positive, mostly negative, or roughly balanced between positive and negative characteristics? Are you surprised by this, or is it basically what you expected?

D. Finally, look back to part (A) of this exercise where you wrote down the ten adjectives that you thought best described your personality. To what extent would you modify that description based on what you have learned from part (B)? If modifications are necessary, in the space below write a revised list of just ten adjectives that you now think best capture your most important personality characteristics:

We will refer often to the results of this exercise in later chapters of this workbook, and you will have an opportunity to use the results in a variety of interesting ways to learn more about yourself and about people around you. For the moment, let's change our focus to another of the key questions mentioned in the chapter.

Where Am I Going?

A. Take as much time as necessary to answer the following question on a separate sheet of paper: "What are my most important lifetime goals?" Put down whatever comes into your mind, no matter how general or abstract it may seem. Your goals may include personal, family, career, social, and spiritual goals. You may want to put your list aside for a few days and come back to it when you are ready to make alterations. When you think you have a fairly complete set of your most important goals, write them in the space below:

B. Take a new sheet of paper and answer the following question: "How would I like to spend the next three years?" Here you will want to list important short-range goals. Again, you may want to put the list aside for a while and then make alterations until you are satisfied with the result. Record your final set of three-year goals here:

C. Finally, on another sheet of paper, answer the following question: "If I knew my life would end six months from today, how would I live until then?" This question should help you determine whether there are things that are important to you that you are not doing or even considering now. When you have made additions, deletions, and other changes and have a satisfactory answer, write it in the space below:

D. Compare the goals you have listed in (A), (B), and (C). Be particularly aware of goals that appear on all lists or common themes that run throughout your lists. In the space below, write down the three goals you think are most important as a result of this exercise.

In six months or a year (or five years or more), you will find it interesting to look back to your answers to these questions and to consider whether you have moved closer to realizing some of your most important goals, to think about whether you should modify (or delete) some of your goals, and perhaps to identify those goals that will require more effort to achieve. In the meantime, you might consider sharing this exercise with people close to you: after they work on all their own answers independently, share your answers with them and talk together about the similarities and differences in your goals.

How Do I Get There?

A. Again using a separate sheet of paper, make two columns. At the top of one write *Strengths* and at the top of the other write *Weaknesses*. Then list under *Strengths* those areas in which you think you are especially skilled, competent, or capable. You may find it helpful to refer to the list of competencies on page 14 of the textbook for ideas of things to include. Similarly, list under *Weaknesses* those areas in which you think you are less competent. Take all the time you need in preparing these lists; add to them and modify them until you are satisfied that they are reasonably complete and accurate. Then write your final list of competencies in the columns below.

Strengths:

Weaknesses:

B. Is your list of strengths about the same length as your list of weaknesses? Longer? Shorter? If one list is significantly longer than the other, consider asking someone who knows you well to help you add to the shorter list so that the two lists are about equal in length.

C. Now compare your list of strengths and weaknesses with the three most important goals you listed in (D) on page 6 of this workbook. Some of your strengths are likely to help you achieve those goals; put an asterisk (*) in front of those strengths, underline them, or highlight them in some way. These are competencies that will be important in helping you achieve your most important goals. They are competencies you will want to continue to strengthen and develop in the coming years. However, if you are like most people, you will also find that some of your weaknesses may make it more difficult to achieve your most important goals. Underline a few of these weaknesses. These are areas you may need to improve if you are to achieve your goals.

As you read through the remainder of the textbook, be particularly alert for suggestions about how you might begin to improve your strengths and minimize or eliminate your weaknesses. When you have finished this course, come back to your list and map out a deliberate course of action that will help you further strengthen your skills over the next few years.

The Quest for Understanding

1. Review an early article written by a psychologist. Pinpoint the author's attitude toward human nature. Is it evil, good, or neutral? List examples of relevant sentences. (pp. 58-60)

Evil	Good	Neutral

2. Visit your religious leader and ask him/her to define for you human nature. List his/her specific points.
   In what way are your views similar and/or different from those of your religious leader? List your views. (pp. 58-60)

3. Meet with two other members of your class. Each of you should then assume the role of a person who displays the characteristics of the id, ego, and superego. Discuss the value of an education and note the key points made by each person. (pp. 29-32)

Id Person	Ego Person	Superego Person

4. Think of one of your friends who is not responding effectively with respect to some maladaptive problem (e.g., drinking). How would you deal with that problem if you were a psychoanalyst, a humanist, or a believer in the social-learning model? List specific guidance each would use. (Alternatively you could meet with two other members of your class and assume the therapist role of the three theories, then list specific approaches.) (pp. 29-58)

Points of Guidance		
Psychoanalysis	Humanists	Social-Learning

Exploration

As you were reading Chapter 2, you undoubtedly found that one or two of the models matched your own ideas about human nature more closely than did the other model(s). In this exercise, you will have an opportunity to determine more precisely the similarity of your ideas to each of the three models. I will then have some suggestions for ways in which you can learn more about these several viewpoints if you are interested.

Following you will find eight pairs of statements about human nature. The statements on the left and right sides of the page represent opposite extremes of a particular issue. If you agree strongly with the statement on the left of the page, circle 1. If you agree strongly with the statement on the right of the page, circle 5. If your views fall somewhere between these two extremes, circle the number that best represents your position. Do this for each of the eight pairs of statements.

1. In order to understand a person's personality, you have to consider their inherited characteristics and their internal physical and biological makeup.

1 ....2 ....3 ....4 5

Personality is shaped entirely by experience and by interaction with the environment. Heredity and biology are unimportant.

2. You can't fully understand one particular characteristic of a person without considering that person as a whole. The same characteristic can mean different things to different people.

1 ....2 ....3 ....4 5

You need not consider the person as a whole in order to understand some aspect of their personality. Behavior can be understood without knowing how it is related to all other aspects of the person.

3. In order to understand a person's personality, you have to see the world through their eyes, to understand the unique way they experience and interpret the environment.

1 ....2 ....3 ....4 5

Behavior is influenced largely by events in the environment. It is possible to understand behavior without needing to know how the person uniquely experiences the environment.

4. Human beings are goal-directed and purposeful. Much behavior is a result of their efforts to reach their goals.

1 ....2 ....3 ....4 5

People are reactive: they respond to external events. It is not necessary to consider goals and purposes in order to understand behavior.

5. People control their own behavior. They are not machines controlled by the environment. Nor are they governed by deep, hidden forces that are beyond their control. They choose to behave as they do, and they are personally responsible for their acts.

1 ....2 ....3 ....4 5

Our behavior is controlled by forces that are normally beyond our awareness and beyond our control. Our feeling that we are free to act as we wish is an illusion.

6. People are motivated primarily by a desire to minimize tension, to maintain the "status quo." They resist challenges, stimulation, and change.

1 ....2 ....3 ....4 5

People are motivated to grow, to seek challenges and new experiences, to stretch themselves and, in the process, to develop more fully as human beings.

7. A person's basic personality is determined during childhood. Although superficial changes may occur in later years, the underlying personality structure remains unchanged.

1 ....2 ....3 ....4 5

Personality can change throughout the course of life. Growth and development are constant. We are not bound by the past.

8. Each person is unique. You cannot fully understand a person's personality unless you come to understand that person as a unique human being.

1 ....2 ....3 ....4 5

People are basically quite similar. You can understand a person's behavior without having to consider the ways in which he or she differs from everyone else.

When you have rated each of the eight statements, record your ratings in the column headed "Your rating" in the table below. Now look at the column headed "Contemporary psychoanalytic model." The numbers in this column represent the ratings that a contemporary psychoanalytic theorist would be likely to give to each of the eight pairs of statements.[1] For each statement, determine the difference between your rating and that of the psychoanalytic model and enter the difference in the column provided (enter numbers without plus and minus signs—a difference of +2 or −2 would be entered as 2). Repeat this process for each of the other two models: compare your rating for each statement with the corresponding rating for that model and enter the differences in the spaces provided.

---

[1]The ratings for each model are based on the following sources: Hall and Lindzey (1978), Hjelle and Ziegler (1981), Engler (1985), Hergenhahn (1984), Shultz (1981), Smith and Vetter (1982), Corsini (1977).

Statement #	Your rating	Contemporary psychoanalytic model	Difference	Humanistic model	Difference	Social-learning model	Difference
1	_____	2	_____	3	_____	5	_____
2	_____	2	_____	1	_____	5	_____
3	_____	2	_____	1	_____	4	_____
4	_____	2	_____	1	_____	4	_____
5	_____	4	_____	1	_____	4	_____
6	_____	4	_____	5	_____	1	_____
7	_____	2	_____	5	_____	3	_____
8	_____	3	_____	1	_____	5	_____
		TOTAL =	_____	TOTAL =	_____	TOTAL =	_____

When you are finished, add the differences for each model and put the total in the space provided at the bottom of each column. Look now at the differences between your ratings and those of the contemporary psychoanalytic model. If the total of the differences is zero, then your beliefs about these eight aspects of human nature are virtually identical to those of the psychoanalytic model; on the other hand, a score of 26 would indicate that you disagree strongly with the contemporary psychoanalytic model on these eight aspects of human nature. You can repeat the process for the other two models: in each case strong agreement between your views and those of the model would be indicated by a difference score of zero. For the humanistic model, strong disagreement would result in a difference score of 30; for the behavioral model, a difference score of 27 would indicate strong disagreement.

A. Based on your understanding of the three models, as well as the exercise you have just completed, which of the models comes closest to capturing your own view of human nature?

Now look back to the portions of Chapter 2 that described that model, as well as the table on page 65, and briefly summarize the four or five most important points on which you agree most strongly with this model.

B. Part of a full answer to the question "Who am I?" is a description of the ways in which you are like all other human beings. Reword the principles you selected in (A) so that they describe you; that is, rewrite them in the form "Like all other human beings, I am. . . ."

C. You may want to do some additional reading about these various models of human nature. The sources listed in the footnote on page 10 of this workbook are an excellent starting place. In addition, you will find the following sources extremely useful (most of them are available in paperback):

Psychoanalytic model

Brenner, C. (1974). *An elementary textbook of psychoanalysis.* New York: Anchor Books.
Erikson, E.H. (1963). *Childhood and society.* New York: W.W. Norton.
Roazen, P. (1976). *Erik H. Erikson: The power and limits of a vision.* New York: Free Press.

Humanistic-existential model

Maslow, A. (1968). *Toward a psychology of being* (2d ed.). New York: Van Nostrand.
May, R. (Ed.). (1969). *Existential psychology.* New York: Random House.
Rogers, C. (1961). *On becoming a person.* Boston: Houghton Mifflin.
Shaffer, J.B.P. (1978). *Humanistic psychology.* Englewood Cliffs, N.J.: Prentice-Hall.

Social-learning model

Bandura, A. (1977). *Social learning theory.* Englewood Cliffs, N.J.: Prentice-Hall.
Skinner, B.F. (1948). *Walden Two.* New York: Macmillan.
Skinner, B.F. (1971). *Beyond freedom and dignity.* New York: Bantam Books.

Problems of Adjustment

Activities

1. Interview a person working at a crisis center (perhaps a group of classmates can get together) and ask him/her what are the most frequent problems he/she hears about and the primary advice and guidance he/she gives in each case.

	Most Common Problems	Advice
1.		
2.		
3.		
4.		
5.		

2. Imagine you are in turn a Type A and B person. How would you deal with these problems? (p. 96)

	Type A	Type B
1. Poor grades in class		
2. The breakup of a relationship		
3. A demotion on your first job		

3. Listen for one hour to a radio music program. List the songs which deal with various types of stress. (pp. 72-92, 98)

Radio Program

Song Titles	Types of Stress	Types of Eustress

Surveying Your Perspective

Surveying Your Anxiety

Below you will find a survey which might provide some information on the state of your anxiety. Surveys, of course, should be taken in the spirit of exploration and not as a definitive statement on your mental health. Also, a person's anxiety may change from time to time. Therefore, assess the results as only one source of information. Please consult the instructions used in Chapter 2.

1 2 3 4 5   1. Life is generally pleasant.

1 2 3 4 5   2. Others seem more happy than I.

1 2 3 4 5   3. I have difficulty in making up my mind.

1 2 3 4 5   4. I constantly worry.

1 2 3 4 5   5. I feel joyful.

1 2 3 4 5   6. I am basically insecure.

1 2 3 4 5   7. Nothing much disturbs my peace of mind.

1 2 3 4 5   8. I am tired much of the time.

1 2 3 4 5   9. My state of mind is tranquil.

1 2 3 4 5   10. Compared to others I am content.

Reverse weights for items 1, 5, 7, 9, and 10, and divide by number of items. Note your score here: _____. A score higher than 3 reflects some anxiety, scores lower than 3 reflect lower anxiety.

Altruism

Frustrations of various types are major sources of life stress. Aggression is one response to frustration. The following scale measures "aggression" employing widely varying behaviors and situations. The format for the scale and scoring procedure is *different* from the preceding scales and surveys used.

The following is a study of what the public thinks about a number of important social issues. You may find yourself agreeing with some of the statements and disagreeing with other statements. Put a check mark (√) beside those statements with which you agree; put a cross (X) beside those with which you disagree.

Poor people are the responsibility of society	8.30
War brings out both good and bad qualities in men	5.70
The Jews have helped build this country	7.33
Idealists must be brought back to reality, even though it may upset them	4.40
A child should be forced to obey if he does not do so immediately	3.09
School teachers need more freedom to discipline students as they feel necessary	4.19
More people would favor communism if they only knew something about it	6.23
The white race must be kept pure at all cost, even if other races have to be killed off	1.04
If Germany had been wiped out by the war, the world would be better off now	1.57
Children will usually see how far they can go	5.41
I am my brother's keeper	9.50
A child who steals money from his parents should be given understanding, help, and forgiveness	9.61
We should guarantee food for hungry people	10.60
America surpasses other countries only in prosperity	6.50
The practice of executing murderers is just and necessary	2.75
The best way to eliminate the Communist menace in this country is to control the Jewish element which guides it	2.29
Execution of criminals is absolutely never justified	9.28

To calculate your score add up the scale values (listed by each item) of all the items with which you agree, divide by the number of items you agree with. If your score is higher than 6 you score toward the altruistic end of the scale, if lower than 6 you agree more with aggressive items. Note your score here: _____.

Aggression as measured by the Aggression scale was related to severity of aggression training; to chauvinistic nationalism; and to the cynical manipulation of others.

Reference

Larsen, K.S. (1971). Aggression-Altruism: A scale and some data on its reliability and validity. *Journal of Personality Assessment, 36*(8), 276-81.

Daily Hassles

Listed are a number of ways you can feel hassled. Circle the hassle which has affected you recently, and indicate the number corresponding to severity of hassle.

Severity
    0—No hassle
    1—Somewhat hassled
    2—Moderately hassled
    3—Extremely hassled

1. Concern about your weight   _____
2. Health of some family member   _____
3. Rising tuition   _____
4. Physical appearance   _____
5. Drug problems   _____
6. Sex-related problems   _____
7. Meaning of life   _____
8. Being lonely   _____
9. Fear of rejection   _____
10. Not sleeping well   _____
11. Love-related problems   _____
12. Worrying about getting ahead   _____
13. Other _____   _____

Add your score for all items circled, divide by the number of items. Note your score here: _____. A score of 0-1 is somewhat hassled, 1-2 moderately hassled, 2-3 extremely hassled.

The survey (p. 16) helps you to pinpoint areas which are hassles in your daily life. These are areas in which you may wish to improve using the helpful guidance of your chapter or resources in your community. As in the case of all surveys, the form above provides helpful indications of problem areas, but is not a definitive statement. If you have questions, discuss them with your counselor or professor.

Exploration

Think for a moment about a particularly stressful experience you had in the past or are having now. It might be something that happened long ago but was so stressful you still think about it. Or it might be something more recent. It might even be something that keeps happening—a chronic problem of some sort that is continually stressful. Whatever experience you choose, it should be important to you and something you would like to understand better and perhaps cope with more effectively. We will use this experience in the next several exercises as well to illustrate stress, stress reactions, and both effective and ineffective ways of coping with stress. So pick a stressful experience you would really like to understand better and that you are willing to think about at some length.

A. Now that you have chosen your stressful experience, describe the source of the stress in some detail in the space below. What caused the stress? Was it a case of frustration, conflict, pressure, or self-imposed stress—or some combination of these? As you write your answer, refer back to the section of the textbook that discusses the various sources of stress (pages 75-77) and think about whether each source discussed there played any role in your experience. Your objective here is to understand as fully as possible the sources of the stress (not how you reacted to it or felt about it or tried to cope with it—we will cover those in subsequent exercises).

B. Often, when people are answering the first part of this exercise they discover that their stressful experience had more causes than they were aware of at first. For example, what seemed to be a case of frustration turned out also to be a case of severe conflict or pressure. Or they discover that there was a good deal of self-imposed stress added on top of an already stressful event. Did this occur when you were writing about your experience in (A)? If so, what were a few of the sources that surprised you the most? You might find it easier to answer this question if you start out by writing "Until I wrote about my experience, I hadn't realized. . . ."

C. If you followed the suggestions at the start of this exercise, you chose a particularly stressful event to write about. Why was (is) that event so terribly stressful for you? Refer back to the section of the textbook on factors that influence the severity of stress (pages 93-97) and try to determine which of those factors made the experience particularly stressful for you.

D. Finally, look back over your answers in (A), (B), and (C) (and read back through Chapter 3 in the textbook if you think that would be helpful) and then try to answer the following questions: Would most other people have found the experience as stressful as you did? Would they have found it more stressful or less stressful? Why do you think so?

We will look at other aspects of this stressful experience in the next several chapters in an effort to help you understand it more fully.

Reactions to Stressful Events

1. Make a list of all events that caused you stress today. What were your emotional reactions or feelings? How did it make you feel physically? (pp. 72-92)

Stressful Events	Emotional Reaction	Physical Reaction

2. Give a personal example for five defense mechanisms.

Defense Mechanisms	Examples
Denial	1.
Fantasy	
Rationalization	2.
Projection	
Displacement	3.
Regression	
Compensation	4.
Acting out	
Undoing	5.
Emotional insulation	
Intellectualization	

3. What can you do to preserve your mental health? Discuss with another student and generate a list of "10 commandments" which aid in promoting good mental health. Examine such issues as having close friends; finding your unhappiness in something which can be modified; taking full credit for your accomplishments; unique strengths and abilities; putting distance between yourself and your problems; don't dwell on the past; learn from failures; goals; time to meditate, etc. (p. 93)

Commandments
1.
2.
3.
4.
5.
6.
7.
8.
9.
10.

4. Write a paragraph on Plato's statement ". . . all diseases of the body proceed from the mind or the soul."

Exploration

At the end of Chapter 3 you described in some detail a particularly stressful event, the sources of the stress, and the reasons why it was (or is) particularly stressful for you. In the section below, we will try to clarify the various ways in which you responded to that stressful event. You may find it helpful to re-read your answers to the Self-Discovery exercise at the end of Chapter 3 before you continue.

A. In the space below, write down a list of all the physiological reactions you experienced as a result of the stressful event. Take your time and make your list as complete as possible. If you run out of ideas, you may find that re-reading pages 106-117 in this chapter will jog your memory. When you think your list of physiological reactions is complete, continue to the next portion of this exercise.

Physiological responses to stressful event:

B. Now, in the space below, write a list of all the emotional reactions you experienced as a result of the stressful event. Take your time and make your list as complete as possible. If you run out of ideas, you may find that re-reading pages 117-122 in this chapter will jog your memory. When you think your list of physiological reactions is complete, continue to the next portion of this exercise.

Emotional responses to stressful event:

C. In the space below, list each of the defense mechanisms you are aware of using to help you cope with the stressful event. You may find it helpful to refer to the chart on page 123 and the discussion on pages 122-130 to help you identify the different defenses you may have used (or are using).

Defense-oriented responses to stressful event:

D. Now think for a moment of several other especially stressful events you have encountered in your life and your responses to them. Put an asterisk (*) beside any of the responses you listed in (A), (B), or (C) that you also experienced in these other stressful events. These starred items are the responses that you tend to have when you are confronted with stress. If you think of other responses that you often experienced under stress that do not appear in (A), (B), or (C), list them in the space below with an asterisk.

Other frequent responses to stressful events:

The asterisked items on your lists are early-warning signs that you are experiencing an unusual degree of stress. In the future, when you notice yourself reacting in these ways, you may find it useful to take a moment to identify the source of the stress and to decide whether it is something with which you should deal directly. In the next chapter, we will discuss ways of coping with various stressors.

Effective Methods of Coping with Stress

Activities

1. Discuss five stressful situations. How would you currently cope with these life events? Evaluate ways these strategies may be improved. (pp. 131-132)

	Stress Situation	Current Strategy	Improvement
1.			
2.			
3.			
4.			
5.			

2. Think of some problem which is currently giving you stress. Then, brainstorm a solution. Now sit down with someone from the class (or someone you know from elsewhere). List the variety of options available to you and try to generate

many solutions, even if some appear silly. From multiple options one or several may emerge as workable solutions.

Brainstorming Solutions

1.

2.

3.

4.

5.

6.

7.

8.

Which of these solutions is/are workable?

1.

2.

3.

3. Communing with nature is a great way to relax. Others have suggested that exercise such as walking or jogging has beneficial effects. Take a nature walk (or walk in a park), and at a different time walk rapidly for one mile (as your health permits). Note how you feel after each exercise.

My Feelings

Communing with nature

Taking a rapid walk

---

4. (a) Read a daily newspaper and list all the situations which cause you anxiety; (b) distinguish those which can realistically impact on your life with some degree

of certainty; and (c) list what you can do about each situation if you made an effort. (pp. 148-152)

Anxiety-Provoking Situations 1	Those Likely to Impact Your Life 2	What Can Be Done? 3

5. To cope with stress it is important that we set goals which are compatible with our abilities and opportunities. For your career goal, describe the necessary aptitudes you must possess, competencies to achieve, and opportunities currently in your field. If necessary, seek information from your guidance and counseling center to answer these guidelines. (p. 168)

Necessary Aptitudes	Necessary Competencies	Current Opportunities

Surveying Your Perspective

Touching Behavior

A major source of stress is an inability to show feelings for members of one's own and opposite sex.

"Understanding attitudes toward same sex touching is crucial for a complete understanding of sexual behavior. Not only are same sex touching attitudes a key to heterosexual adjustment (Mehrabian, 1971), but they also relate to general well-being (for example, Jourard, 1966; Silverman, Pressman, & Bartel, 1973). Same sex attitudes may reflect different patterns of sex-role training rigidity, with behavioral consequences for both same sex and heterosexual relations, and on attitudes toward homosexuality.

"Few would disagree that touching another person is a significant act with psychological consequences. Yet, as Hall (1966) notes, investigators have failed to grasp the importance of touching in keeping 'the person related to the world in which he lives' (p. 57). The limited research effort is perhaps itself a reflection of a widespread touching taboo socialized during childhood. According to Jourard (1966), this touch taboo 'has produced a scotoma of our professional vision, making us describe man in our textbooks as if he did not get closer to his fellow than a foot or so' (p. 221). Research in the last decade, however, has demonstrated convincingly the important consequences of touching behavior (Kennell, Slyter, & Klaus, 1970). On the whole, the literature supports the facilitative and positive effects of touching (Aguilera, 1967; Boderman, Freed, & Kinnucan, 1972; Breed & Ricci, 1973; Cooper & Bowles, 1973; Fisher, Rytting & Heslin, 1976; Pattison, 1973)." (p. 265)

Same Sex Touching Scale SSTS

(Use same instructions as in Chapter 2.)

1 2 3 4 5   1. Touch is important in my communication with others of my sex.

1 2 3 4 5   2. I appreciate a hug from a person of my sex when I need comforting.

1 2 3 4 5   3. I enjoy touching persons of my sex who are comfortable with touching.

1 2 3 4 5   4. I enjoy touching some persons of the same sex.

1 2 3 4 5   5. I sometimes enjoy the physical contact while hugging persons of the same sex.

1 2 3 4 5   6. I would feel comfortable embracing a close friend of the same sex while fully clothed.

1 2 3 4 5   7. I am comfortable putting my arm around the shoulders of persons of my sex.

1 2 3 4 5   8. I sometimes enjoy hugging friends of the same sex.

1 2 3 4 5   9. I sometimes like some persons of the same sex putting an arm around my shoulders.

1 2 3 4 5   10. I enjoy being touched by someone of the same sex.

1 2 3 4 5   11. Physical expression of affection between persons of the same sex is healthy.

1 2 3 4 5   12. I am comfortable giving a massage to someone of my sex.

1 2 3 4 5   13. When I am tense, I would enjoy receiving a neck and shoulder massage from a person of the same sex.

1 2 3 4 5   *14. I would rather avoid touching persons of the same sex.

1 2 3 4 5   *15. I feel uncomfortable touching in a relationship with someone of the same sex.

1 2 3 4 5   *16. Touching between persons of the same sex should be limited to a handshake only.

1 2 3 4 5   17. I like the feeling of warmth I sometimes get while embracing close friends of the same sex.

1 2 3 4 5   18. When I have a headache, having someone of the same sex massage my neck and shoulders feels good.

1 2 3 4 5   19. I sometimes hug members of my sex when I feel close to them.

1 2 3 4 5   20. It pleases me to see persons of the same sex hug each other in greeting.

Reverse weights for the starred (*) items, sum for all items, and divide by number of items. Note your score here: _____. If your score is more than 3, you are somewhat positive toward same sex touching; if less, you are somewhat negative.

"We suggest that same sex touching attitudes are important to the psychological well-being of the individual and that same sex touching ease has direct implications of heterosexual adjustment. It could be hypothesized that the lack of intimacy in some heterosexual relationships is influenced by carry-over fears based on same sex taboos in our society. To understand the full complexity of sexual behavior, researchers must examine more closely the male unease (or negative attitudes) and its influence on heterosexual intimacy" (p. 276).

Reference

Larsen, K.S., and Le Roux, J. (1984). A study of same sex touching attitudes: Scale development and personality predictors. *The Journal of Sex Research, 20*(3), 264-78.

Exploration

The Self-Discovery exercises in the past two chapters have helped you to analyze a particularly stressful event in your life. In Chapter 3 you analyzed the reasons why that event was (or is) particularly stressful, and in Chapter 4 you analyzed your various reactions to the event. In this exercise you will have an opportunity to think about the ways in which you tried to cope with that stressful event and to think systematically about how you could have responded (or could respond now) more effectively to the stressful event.

A. On a separate sheet of paper, write down a list of all the techniques you used (or are using) to try to cope with the stressful event you described in Chapters 5 and 6. Take your time and make your list as complete as possible. If you run out of ideas, you may find that re-reading pages 156-165 in this chapter will jog your memory.

When you think your list of coping strategies is complete, list the strategies you used (or are using) in the proper category below. If you are unsure of which category a particular coping response belongs, refer to pages 158-160 of this chapter.

Attack responses:

Withdrawal responses:

Compromise responses:

Before you continue, review your list of responses to the stressful event to be sure that you have mentioned all of the coping responses you used.

B. Now use the three criteria discussed on page 162 to help you determine how effective your coping strategies were. Then briefly answer the following questions:

How well did your actions meet the adjustive demand?

Did your actions meet your personal needs?

Were your actions compatible with the well-being of others?

C. Now we will try to formulate a more appropriate way of coping with the stressful situation using the strategy described on pages 158-162. You have already thoroughly evaluated the stress situation (Chapter 3 Self-Discovery), so the next step is to formulate alternatives. On a separate sheet of paper, list all the reactions from the list in (A) that you believe were or are appropriate and helpful ways of responding to the situation. Then use brainstorming to add new ideas to your list (be sure to read the description of brainstorming on page 161). Try to add as many ideas as possible to your list, regardless of how silly or bizarre they may seem to you. Don't rush this process. When the flow of ideas starts to slow down, set the list aside and then return to it after a while to add new possibilities that have occurred to you. You will probably find it helpful to re-read pages 156-165 where I discussed a number of effective coping techniques. Consider asking your close friends what they would have done under similar circumstances, and add their ideas to the list. Your goal is to list everything you can possibly think of that you could have done or could be doing now to cope with the stressful event.

D. When your list is complete, weigh the costs and benefits associated with each alternative as well as its probability of success (be sure to re-read pages 161-163 for a more detailed description of this selection process). Your goal is to identify perhaps a dozen particularly good alternatives for coping with the stressful event. When you have made your selection, list your best alternatives in the space below:

E. In the course of this exercise, you should have discovered that there were many more ways to cope with the stressful event than you realized at first. This is almost always the case. In the future, when you are trying to cope with an unusually stressful event, take the time to analyze the sources of stress, to analyze your reactions, and to make a list of alternatives using the steps you have followed in these three Self-Discovery exercises. With practice, you will find yourself becoming more skillful at identifying sources of stress and effective responses to stress, so that eventually you will seldom have to go through all the written exercises to come up with good alternative courses of action.

If the stressful event is one with which you are still trying to cope, try some of these alternatives and use feedback to evaluate their effectiveness and to modify your strategy (see pages 154-165 for helpful suggestions at this stage).

Maladaptive Behavior

1. Collect advertisements for cigarettes aimed at men and women. What appeals does the tobacco industry employ to encourage addiction?

   _____

   Persuasion Appeals

   _____

   For Men   For Women

   _____

2. Make a list of situations which make you anxious. Rank order these situations from most to least anxiety-producing. Perhaps talking to a member of the opposite sex causes a great deal of anxiety, whereas for someone else speaking to someone in authority produces discomfort. (p. 180)

   _____

   List

   _____

   For one or two of these situations, devise a desensitization experiment. In other words, gradually approximate your goal of mastering your anxiety in several small steps. For example, if you are fearful of speaking to a member of the opposite sex at a party, you may try the following steps for separate occasions:

a. Step inside the party for five minutes.
b. Look at a member of the opposite sex (establish eye contact).
c. Talk briefly to a member of the opposite sex.
d. Try for a minimum of a fifteen-minute conversation.

Rank Order of Anxiety-Producing Situations	Step-by-Step Plan for Desensitizing Yourself to Master the Anxiety

3. Contact your local Alcoholics Anonymous chapter in the phone directory and attend an open Alcoholics Anonymous meeting. Write a short report on what you learned about the causes of alcoholism; the physical, psychological, and spiritual effects on the alcoholic; and the effects on the alcoholic's family. (pp. 198-199)

Causes	Effects on Alcoholic	Effects on Alocholic's Family

Surveying Your Perspective

Marijuana Usage

Marijuana usage is a controversial topic in many states. Occasional and regular usage has spread through substantial parts of the population. Efforts to legalize consumption and growth for private usage is an ongoing effort. How do you feel about marijuana usage? The following questions should be answered using the preceding instructions.

1 2 3 4 5   1. The sale of less than one ounce of marijuana should not be restricted.

1 2 3 4 5   2. I do not agree with the policy of spraying harmful pesticides on marijuana fields.

1 2 3 4 5   *3. Marijuana is a definite deterrent to the social well-being of society.

1 2 3 4 5   *4. I would not have anything to do with an illegal substance like marijuana.

1 2 3 4 5   *5. I encourage my friends *not* to smoke marijuana.

1 2 3 4 5   *6. The penalty for possession of marijuana should be stiffened.

1 2 3 4 5   7. People should be allowed to grow as much marijuana as they deem necessary for their personal use.

1 2 3 4 5   8. Being around others smoking does not bother me.

1 2 3 4 5   9. People of all ages should be allowed to make their own choices about their own use of marijuana.

1 2 3 4 5   10. I enjoy marijuana at social activities.

1 2 3 4 5   11. Marijuana paraphernalia should be easily obtainable.

1 2 3 4 5   12. Marijuana should be legalized and taxed.

1 2 3 4 5   *13. The use of marijuana is addictive.

1 2 3 4 5   *14. I feel marijuana is a harmful drug.

1 2 3 4 5   *15. If people are smoking marijuana at a party, I leave.

1 2 3 4 5   *16. People who smoke marijuana should be punished.

1 2 3 4 5   *17. I do not like the smell of marijuana smoke.

1 2 3 4 5   18. Responsible adults should be allowed to make their own choices about their own use of marijuana.

1 2 3 4 5   *19. I am opposed to the legalization of marijuana.

1 2 3 4 5   *20. Only stupid people smoke marijuana.

1 2 3 4 5   21. Marijuana is something that everyone should try at least once.

1 2 3 4 5   *22. People who drive under the influence of marijuana are as dangerous as drunk drivers.

1 2 3 4 5   23. I feel that marijuana should be as socially acceptable as drinking is.

1 2 3 4 5   *24. Marijuana should be totally banned.

Reverse the weights for starred (*) items. Add your score for all items and divide by number of items. Note your score here: _____. If larger than 3, you are positive toward marijuana use; if less, you are negative.

Exploration

Quite often as people begin to reach the limits of their ability to cope effectively with stress, mildly maladaptive behaviors begin to appear. These behaviors serve as an early-warning signal that we are on the verge of being overwhelmed by the situation in which we find ourselves. Each of us differs in the behaviors that provide these early-warning signals. For some people, the first sign is an increase in drug use (such as drinking more alcohol or coffee, or smoking more cigarettes). Other people notice psychophysiological disorders of various kinds (perhaps headaches or indigestion). Still others find it difficult to sleep or experience emotional outbursts (anger, crying). It is useful to be attentive to the presence of these early warning signs and to use them as helpful signals that the time has come to deal more directly with the source of stress and our reactions to it. In this Self-Discovery exercise, you will learn to identify your own early-warning signals.

A. Review your answers to the Self-Discovery exercise in Chapter 4. In the spaces below, write down all the physiological, emotional, or defense-oriented responses that you starred or asterisked in that exercise (those were the responses you tended to have most often when confronted by stress):

1. _____
2. _____
3. _____
4. _____
5. _____
6. _____
7. _____
8. _____
9. _____
10. _____
11. _____
12. _____
13. _____
14. _____
15. _____

16. _____
17. _____
18. _____
19. _____
20. _____

B. Now, refresh your memory of the particularly stressful event you described in the Self-Discovery exercises in Chapters 3-5. Then place a check mark in the space to the left of any maladaptive behaviors in the list below that were triggered by that stressful event (or some other event that was especially stressful for you).

_____ Problems with school or work performance

_____ Difficulty concentrating or making decisions

_____ Sleep disturbances

_____ Emotional outbursts

_____ Loss of emotions and feelings

_____ Preoccupation with the stressful event

_____ Obsessive thoughts or impulses

_____ Stuttering, tics

_____ Compulsive behaviors, rigid procedures

_____ Loss of appetite

_____ Reduced interest in sex

_____ Loss of interest in hobbies or leisure activities

_____ Extreme agitation

_____ Extreme talkativeness

_____ Feelings of fatigue

_____ Increased argumentativeness

_____ Increased use of drugs or other psychoactive substances

_____ Thoughts of suicide

_____ Blaming others inappropriately

_____ Feelings of depression, hopelessness, or despair

_____ Anxiety, panic, fearfulness

_____ Social withdrawal, feeling distant from others

_____ Illegal behavior (vandalism, reckless driving)

_____ Increased aggressiveness, fighting, abuse of others

_____ _____

_____ _____

_____ _____

_____ _____

_____ _____

_____ _____

_____ _____

_____ _____

    If you have experienced other maladaptive behaviors that do not appear on either list (A) or list (B), add them in the spaces provided and put a check mark in front of them.

    C. Now think about an entirely different stressful event in your life that also led to some maladaptive behaviors. Make a check mark beside those behaviors in the list above (in some cases this may result in two check marks beside an item, while other items will have only one check mark or none at all).

    How do you tend to respond when you are reaching the limits of your ability to cope with unusual stress? One way to begin developing an answer is to study the lists you prepared in (A) and (B) above. All the items on list (A) are reactions you tend to have when under stress; the items with two check marks in list (B) are also maladaptive behaviors that tend to appear as early warning signs when you are under unusual stress. Add to these lists any other early-warning signs that you tend to display when you are under particularly severe stress. Also, you might ask some close friends or family members to tell you about any characteristic behaviors they notice when you are under stress. Add those signs to your list.

    The resulting list will be useful to you in the future. It alerts you to the various ways in which you uniquely signal to yourself and to others that you are reaching the limits of your ability to cope with stress. These signals are early-warning signs that you need to deal more effectively with the stress you are experiencing, perhaps by repeating the Self-Discovery exercises in Chapters 3 and 5 or by seeking professional assistance (as we will discuss in the next chapter).

Psychotherapy and Counseling

Activities

1. To save time, perhaps as a group you may seek an appointment with several specialists in counseling and psychotherapy listed in your book (p. 218). While it simplifies the therapeutic process, ask the specialist to identify the three most frequent problems they assist people with, and the typical therapeutic guidance provided for these problems.

	Type of Personnel		Problems	Typical Guidance
1.		a.		
		b.		
		c.		
2.		a.		
		b.		
		c.		
3.		a.		
		b.		
		c.		

It is important to recognize that you are only role playing in the activity which follows. The activity serves to provide you with some insight to the therapeutic process, but does not, of course, qualify you as an amateur therapist.

2. Meet with a fellow class member and take turns playing the role of patient and therapist. As the patient, take on the role of some type of maladaptive behavior discussed in Chapter 6. As therapist, your task is to discover the type of problem. In doing so, obtain various types of assessment information. What would you recommend, counseling or psychotherapy? (pp. 223-226)

3. With a fellow class member discuss the relative merits of humanistic-existential therapies versus the social-learning approach. What are the strengths and weaknesses of each approach?

	Humanistic-existential	Social-learning
Strengths		
Weaknesses		

4. Find an early book dealing with sex therapy. Compare the recommendations made in that book with those made by Masters and Johnson in your text. In which way have things changed?

Sex Therapy Recommendations	
Early therapist	
Masters and Johnson	

5. Ask if you may "sit in" on a meeting of some encounter group or group dynamics class held in your community or college. What was the group format, climate, and process? (p. 245)

Group Format   Group Process

Surveying Your Perspective

Your chapter discusses marital therapy and divorce. What are your attitudes toward divorce? Complete the following scale using the previous instructions for attitude scales.

1 2 3 4 5   *1. Divorce would be my last alternative for resolving my marital conflicts.

1 2 3 4 5   2. Divorce contributes to the equality of women.

1 2 3 4 5   *3. No matter what, I could not divorce.

1 2 3 4 5   4. Divorce is acceptable to me.

1 2 3 4 5   5. Divorce provides a sensible solution to an unhappy marriage.

1 2 3 4 5   *6. If you tried harder in your marriage, you would not have to divorce.

1 2 3 4 5   7. Divorce is socially acceptable.

1 2 3 4 5   8. A divorce is justifiable depending on the wants of the persons involved.

1 2 3 4 5   *9. Divorce is a poor way to resolve an unhappy marriage.

1 2 3 4 5   *10. People who love each other do not divorce.

1 2 3 4 5   11. Divorce is not "below" me.

1 2 3 4 5   12. If I felt divorce to be the only answer to my unresolvable marriage, I would do it.

1 2 3 4 5   13. Most people who divorce have a valid reason for doing so.

1 2 3 4 5   14. Divorce is an option that can remedy an unhealthy situation.

1 2 3 4 5   15. Divorce can be a positive experience.

1 2 3 4 5   16. I consider divorce a reasonable means to an end.

1 2 3 4 5   17. Divorce is a good alternative to a bad marriage.

1	2	3	4	5	18. The evils of divorce should not prevent us from seeing its benefits.
1	2	3	4	5	*19. Divorce reflects a lack of responsibility in carrying out commitments.
1	2	3	4	5	*20. Marriage disputes should be settled without divorce.
1	2	3	4	5	21. Divorce is not disgraceful.

Reverse weights for items 1, 3, 6, 9, 10, 19, 20, and divide by number of items. Note your score here: _____. If your score is higher than 3, you are somewhat positive toward divorce; if lower, somewhat negative.

Reference

Larsen, K.S. (1986). Attitude toward divorce scale. Oregon State University.

Exploration

The decision about when to seek professional assistance is a personal one. We have seen in previous chapters that some people are quite tolerant of stress, while others are less so; some people have developed more effective ways of coping with their problems than have others; and some people have more resources to rely on than do others. In addition, some people are willing to seek professional assistance at the first sign of difficulty, while others wait longer before seeking help. In this exercise we will explore your willingness to consult mental health professionals and also your preference for certain kinds of therapeutic assistance.

A. What kinds of problems would cause you to seek assistance from mental health professionals? In the **Self-Discovery Journal** exercise that accompanies Chapter 6, you identified a number of early warning signals that alert you to the possibility that you are reaching the limits of your ability to cope with life stress. In the space below, indicate some of the kinds of symptoms or problems that would lead you to conclude "I need professional help with my problem."

B. As I pointed out at the beginning of this chapter, the decision to seek professional assistance for personal problems is often a difficult one to make. Do you have concerns, doubts, or worries that would make you hesitate to seek professional assistance even though you think you should do so? If you do, list some of the more important reasons for your hesitation.

C. As we saw in the chapter, therapists vary from being primarily action-oriented and directive at one extreme to being insight-oriented and nondirective at the other extreme. In between these extremes are therapists who at times are directive and at other times nondirective. What type of therapist do you think you would prefer to work with? Indicate your preference by placing an X at the appropriate point on the rating scale below.

Insight-   Action-
oriented;   oriented;
Nondirective   _____ : _____ : _____ : _____ : _____ : _____ : _____   Directive

D. What kinds of mental health professionals are available in your community and how could you reach them if you, or someone close to you, needed their assistance? The college or school you are attending almost certainly has a counseling service staffed by people who can provide an answer to this question; in many cases they will have a list of mental health professionals in the immediate area. The yellow pages in your telephone directory are also useful; look under "Physicians," "Psychologists," "Social Workers," or "Counseling Service." Another good source of information is your state, county, or community mental health center. You can also write to the American Psychiatric Association (1700 18th St. NW, Washington, DC 20009) or the American Psychological Association (1200 17th St. NW, Washington, DC 20036) and ask for assistance in locating mental health professionals in your area.

Self-help groups are easy to find. A national clearinghouse maintains information on self-help groups, and similar clearinghouses have been established in most states. Write to National Self-Help Clearinghouse, 33 West 42nd Street, New York, NY 10036 and ask for their list of regional clearinghouses; enclose a self-addressed stamped envelope. If you need to know the name of your regional clearinghouse immediately, call them at (212) 840-1259. You can then call or write to your regional clearinghouse for information about self-help groups near you that deal with the problem or problems that concern you. The National Clearinghouse can also send you for a small fee information on organizing self-help groups or organizing a self-help clearinghouse in your area, as well as general information about the self-help movement.

Your answers to this exercise and the information you gather about available mental health resources will be most valuable if you keep them for future reference. In the event that you ever feel the need for personal assistance, you will know where to turn. Even if you never need professional assistance, there may be people you love or care for who may have such a need, and you can draw upon this information to help them cope with their stress more effectively.

Development and Adjustment in Childhood and Adolescence

1. Write a brief paragraph report on a child in the sensorimotor stage. How does the child manifest distinctions between self and other objects; object permanence; ability to think about things; planned and purposeful behavior; and mental trial and error? (pp. 271-274)

2. Observe a group of preschool children at play in a park, church, or other location. Note the amount of time spent in various types of play for a one-hour period.

Amount of Time at Play

Ages	Solitary	Parallel	Associative	Cooperative
2-3 years Child 1				
Child 2				
Child 3				

Amount of Time at Play				
Ages	Solitary	Parallel	Associative	Cooperative
4-5 years				
Child 1				
Child 2				
Child 3				

3. List and describe the community based resources, organizations, and locations available to help troubled teenagers.

4. Get together with fellow classmates and examine your local newspaper for the past three months for reports of child abuse. What type of abuse is reported? How do the frequencies compare to those actually reported to the authorities in your community and state?

Frequency			
Type of Abuse	In Newspapers	Community	State
Physical			
Sexual			

During adolescence, social relationships change dramatically as intimate opposite sex friendships begin. A crucial issue is the presence or absence of sexual relations between unmarried young people. How do you feel about this issue? The scale presented below should be completed using the same instructions as used for the survey in Chapter 2.

Premarital Sex Attitudes

1 2 3 4 5   1. Sex is a good way to communicate love in a premarital relationship.

1 2 3 4 5   2. Premarital sex is acceptable for myself.

1 2 3 4 5   *3. When my friends tell me of their premarital sexual experiences, I tend to look at them in a negative way.

1 2 3 4 5   4. Premarital sex is okay if both partners are responsible and use birth control.

1 2 3 4 5   *5. Sex before marriage does not promote a lasting relationship.

1 2 3 4 5   6. Premarital sex is beneficial for a good marriage.

1 2 3 4 5   7. If you are in love, premarital sex is okay.

1 2 3 4 5   *8. I believe I should be married before I enter a sexual relationship.

1 2 3 4 5   9. Premarital sex is okay if both partners are consenting adults.

1 2 3 4 5   10. If my best friend has premarital sex, it's okay for me to do so also.

1 2 3 4 5   11. A marriage commitment is a requirement for a satisfying sexual relationship.

1 2 3 4 5   12. Premarital sex takes the enjoyment out of sex after marriage.

1 2 3 4 5   13. Premarital sex for others is fine.

1 2 3 4 5   14. After a "night on the town" premarital sex is okay.

1 2 3 4 5   *15. Premarital sex is okay for some people but not for me.

1 2 3 4 5   16. If no one gets emotionally hurt from a premarital sexual encounter, then it is okay.

1 2 3 4 5   *17. Premarital sex is wrong.

1 2 3 4 5   *18. Petting is okay but sex should not occur except with one's spouse.

1 2 3 4 5   19. There is no harm in premarital sex.

*Reverse the weights for all the starred (*) items. Sum up for all items and divide by the number of items. Note your score here: _____. If your score is larger than 3, you are somewhat positive toward premarital sex, if less you are somewhat negative.

Reference

Larsen, K.S. (1973). Premarital sex attitudes—A scale and some validity findings. *The Journal of Social Psychology, 90,* 339-40.

Exploration

At the beginning of this chapter, we discussed the kinds of family environments that tend to foster healthy development. In the following section, you will find descriptions of several such environments. Read each description carefully, think back to your own upbringing, and then use the following scale to indicate how strongly you agree with each description as it applies to your own family during the years when you were growing up.

6. __Strongly agree: this statement is a very accurate description; this was definitely true.

5. __Agree: this is generally accurate as a description of my family; this was usually true.

4. __Slightly agree: this is somewhat accurate as a description of my family; more often than not it was true.

3. __Slightly disagree: this is somewhat inaccurate as a description of my family; it was only sometimes true.

2. __Disagree: this is not a very accurate description of my family; it was rarely true.

1. __Strongly disagree: this is a very inaccurate description of my family; it was definitely not true.

As with the other **Self-Discovery Journal** exercises, we urge that you record your answers here so that this book can serve as a permanent record of your thoughts and ideas at this point in your life.

_____ A. There was an atmosphere of love, affection, and warmth. I felt loved and accepted by my parent(s), who were interested in me and in what I was doing. I felt wanted.

_____ B. There were clearly defined standards and limits for acceptable behavior, and I knew what was expected of me. Discipline was both appropriate and realistic. My parents were neither too strict nor too permissive.

_____ C. My parents provided guidance in helping me to decide what was right and wrong, what was worth striving for and what was not. They helped me to set realistic goals that were usually within my reach, and they recognized and enjoyed my successes.

_____ D. My parents encouraged me to seek out new experiences and expand my horizons. They supported and encouraged me when I failed or had difficulty coping with a crisis.

_____ E. My parents were good models. Their own behavior reflected the kinds of values, beliefs, and coping strategies that they were trying to teach me. I could use them as real-life examples of what I wanted to become myself.

_____ F. My parents provided a stimulating environment to explore and stimulated my curiosity. They encouraged me to ask questions and tried to provide (or help me to find) answers. They listened to me when I needed to talk about or explore feelings or problems.

Now pick the description (A-F) that you rated highest (the one that was most accurate as a description of your parents). What lasting effect did that aspect of your parents have on you? What about you might be very different if your parents had not acted that way?

If you have (or expect to have) children of your own, think for a moment about yourself as a parent. You will probably be better at some of these behaviors (A-F above) than at others. Which two or three aspects of parenting do you think you will do best?

Are these the same things that your own parents did well or are they different?

Which do you think will be most difficult for you?

CHAPTER NINE

Development and Adjustment in Adulthood

Activities

1. If you have chosen a career, list ten traits (adjectives) which would describe the personality of a person who would be successful in your chosen occupation. Next check those traits which are part of your personality. (p. 307)

	Traits	Those You Possess
1.		
2.		
3.		
4.		
5.		
6.		
7.		
8.		
9.		
10.		

2. Visit an older person living in a nursing home, and an older person still living at home. In what way (or ways) are their lives different? List some specific differences. (pp. 316-325)

	Physical Condition	Mental Condition	Relationship to Others
Person in nursing home			
Person living at home			

3. Interview a student from another country. In what way/or ways are attitudes toward aging and the old similar or different from our country?
   a. Do aging parents stay with their children?
   b. What is the status of old people?
   c. How active are old people?

Perceptions of Foreign Student	Your Perceptions of U.S. Old People

4. Outline a brief plan for your retirement. What would you do with respect to your relationship with family and friends; your leisure activity; useful work; volunteer effort; travel, etc.?

Surveying Your Perspective

Attitudes Toward Death

"The subject of death has generally been avoided by psychology, and our knowledge of people's attitudes toward death is meager. Intimate studies on death and dying come from medical experts (Kubler-Ross, 1969), and the information is very subjective in nature. Yet, this is one variable which, according to Freud (Hall & Lindzey, 1970), is a major motivation which competes with constructive life forces. What is feared is also likely repressed. That is equally true for psychologists and other groups.

While the fear of death is probably universal, Americans in particular have created a death cult. The cult is characterized by serious attempts at self-deception. This includes open-casket funerals where the dead person is made to appear alive and sleeping in a state of perfect rest. It is doubtful whether these attempts at self-deception really work, and they may in fact only intensify a person's fear of his own death." (p. 687) How do you feel about this issue? The scale presented below should be completed using the same instructions as used for the survey in Chapter 2.

1 2 3 4 5   1. Death is terrible.

1 2 3 4 5   2. I do not worry about dying.

1 2 3 4 5   3. The sight of death is horrifying to me.

1 2 3 4 5   4. Death is a beautiful part of life.

1 2 3 4 5   5. Death is an enemy of the living.

1 2 3 4 5   6. Death is a heavy burden.

1 2 3 4 5   7. There is no reason to be afraid of death.

1 2 3 4 5   8. Death is horrible.

1 2 3 4 5   9. The thought of a loved one's death frightens me.

1 2 3 4 5   10. I wish that I would never die.

1 2 3 4 5   11. People should be afraid to think about death.

1 2 3 4 5   12. The thought of death is peaceful.

1 2 3 4 5   13. I am afraid of death.

1 2 3 4 5   14. Thoughts of death are terrifying to me.

1 2 3 4 5   15. The older I am the greater my fear of death.

1 2 3 4 5   16. Death should be welcomed.

1 2 3 4 5   17. Thoughts of death scare me.

1 2 3 4 5   18. Death is pleasant.

1 2 3 4 5   19. Death is not something I worry about.

1 2 3 4 5   20. The thought of death is extremely frightening.

1 2 3 4 5   21. Death is the worst possible human experience.

1 2 3 4 5   22. I fear death.

1 2 3 4 5   23. A happy life begins with the understanding we must die.

1 2 3 4 5   24. An awareness of the certainty of death is conducive to good mental health.

1 2 3 4 5   25. I resent the idea of having to die.

1 2 3 4 5   26. I would rather not think about death.

1 2 3 4 5   27. Dreams about death frighten me.

1 2 3 4 5   28. The thought of me being dead is extremely unpleasant.

1 2 3 4 5   29. The idea of touching a dead person is frightening.

1 2 3 4 5   30. I try to avoid conversations about death.

1 2 3 4 5   31. The thought of dying really doesn't bother me.

1 2 3 4 5   32. I have not accepted the fact that I must die.

Items 2, 4, 7, 12, 16, 18, 19, 23, 24, and 31 reflect positive attitudes. For a score where high represents a positive attitude toward death, reverse the weights for the remaining items and divide by number of items. Note your score here: _____. If your score is higher than 3, your attitude is somewhat positive, if lower somewhat negative.

"It is possible that the fear of death is chiefly induced by unknown factors involved in dying." Presumably, therefore, the more intimate experience a person has had with death (provided the experience has not traumatized the individual), the more he will be desensitized and accepting of death. By desensitization we mean the reduction of fear as a result of gradual exposure to the feared object. Another factor which makes death unpleasant is the feeling of having failed in achieving self-relevant goals. Even though there are ideological traps in the concept of self-actualization (Maslow, 1968), for example, that the individual is moving toward fulfillment of some soul construct, it cannot be denied that people (depending on the awareness of their potential) see themselves as more or less fulfilled. For those individuals who reach these self-relevant goals, it may be easier to face death. To use a Gestaltist term, there is "closure: in such a person's life." (p. 688)

Reference

Larsen, K.S., Klar, L.R., Rex, G., and White, C. (1974) Attitudes toward death: A desensitization hypothesis. *Psychological Reports, 35,* 687-90.

Exploration

At the beginning of this chapter you answered a number of true-false questions about aging. Without looking back to your earlier answers, answer the same questions again.

T   F   1. The majority of old people (age 65 or older) are senile (for example, have defective memory or are disoriented or demented).

T   F   2. All five senses tend to decline in old age.

T   F   3. Most old people have no interest in, or capacity for, sexual relations.

T   F   4. Most old people have poor lung capacity.

T   F   5. The majority of old people feel miserable most of the time.

T   F   6. Physical strength tends to decline in old age.

T   F   7. At least one-tenth of the aged are living in long-stay institutions (i.e., nursing homes, mental hospitals, homes for the aged, etc.).

T   F   8. Aged drivers have fewer accidents per person than drivers under age 65.

T   F   9. Most older workers cannot work as effectively as younger workers.

T   F   10. About 80 percent of the aged are healthy enough to carry out their normal activities.

T   F   11. Most old people are set in their ways and unable to change.

T   F   12. Old people usually take longer to learn something new.

T   F   13. It is almost impossible for most old people to learn something new.

T   F   14. The reaction time of most old people tends to be slower than the reaction time of younger people.

T   F   15. In general, most old people are pretty much alike.

T   F   16. The majority of old people are seldom bored.

T   F   17. The majority of old people are socially isolated and lonely.

T   F   18. Older workers have fewer accidents than younger workers.

T   F   19. Over 15 percent of the United States population is now age 65 or older.

T   F   20. Most medical practitioners tend to give low priority to the aged.

T   F   21. The majority of older people have incomes below the poverty level (as defined by the federal government).

T   F   22. The majority of old people are working or would like to have some kind of work to do (including housework and volunteer work).

T   F   23. Older people tend to become more religious as they age.

T   F   24. The majority of old people are seldom irritated or angry.

T   F   25. The health and socioeconomic status of older people (compared with that of younger people) in the year 2000 will probably be about the same as now.

Source: Palmore, E. (1977). *The Gerontologist,* 17, 315-320.

A. According to recent research, every odd-numbered question (1, 3, 5, etc.) is false; every even-numbered question (2, 4, 6, etc.) is true. Using this key, score your answers at both the beginning and the end of the chapter. (You will find it easier to respond to later parts of this exercise if you circle the answers that were not correct.) Did your two scores differ? If so, did you do better on the first test or the second? Can you explain why your scores changed?

B. A sample of undergraduates taking introductory sociology at Duke University in the 1970s obtained an average score of 65 percent correct (about 16 out of 25 items correct). How did your two scores compare with that average? If your own score was significantly better or worse than the Duke average, can you explain why?

C. Palmore (1977) suggests that most of the items on this questionnaire provide an indirect meausre of bias in favor of or against the aged. Errors on the following items reflect a negative bias toward the aged: 1, 3, 5, 7, 8, 9, 10, 11, 13, 16, 17, 18, 21, 22, 24, and 25. If you circled your errors on the two tests, it should be easy to determine the number of items on this list that you answered incorrectly on each test and to convert those numbers into percentages (divide the number of errors by 16). For example, if you had nine items wrong, the percentage would be 9/16 or 56 percent. What *percentage* of the 16 questions on this list did you answer incorrectly on each of the two tests?

(I) Percentage incorrect on first test: _____%

(II) Percentage incorrect on second test: _____%

Assuming that 0 percent indicates no negative bias and 100 percent indicates a strong negative bias, did your negative bias increase, decrease, or stay about the same from the beginning to the end of the chapter?

D. Errors on the following items appear to reflect a positive bias (or unrealistically favorable image) toward the aged: 2, 4, 6, 12, and 14. What *percentage* of the 5 questions on this list did you answer incorrectly on each of the two tests (divide the number of errors on these items by 5)?

(III) Percentage incorrect on first test: _____%

(IV) Percentage incorrect on second test: _____%

Assuming that 0 percent indicates no positive bias and 100 percent indicates a strong positive bias, did your positive bias increase, decrease, or stay about the same from the beginning to the end of the chapter?

E. Subtract the percentage in (I) from that in (III) and record the result below. Do the same for (II) and (IV).

(III) − (I) = _____ (first testing)

(IV) − (II) = _____ (second testing)

A negative result in each case indicates an overall negative bias toward the aged, while a positive result indicates an overall positive bias. Did your overall bias change from the beginning to the end of the chapter? If so, to what do you attribute the change? Was it because of a change in negative bias (I versus II), a change in positive bias (III versus IV), or both?

You may be puzzled by the correct answer to some of these questions. A good place to start is by reviewing the material in this chapter where you will find answers to most of the questions. You might also read Palmore's 1977 article in *The Gerontologist* from which the questions were taken. He provides an explanation for each correct answer and also provides references to research studies that confirm the correct answer. Also, any recent textbook on adulthood or aging in your local library or college library should provide the answers to most, if not all, of the questions.

Interpersonal Patterns and Relationships

Activities

1. Think of your closest (intimate) two relationships with boyfriend/girlfriend; husband/wife; parent/child; brother/sister; friend. Now calculate all rewards associated with the relationship (1 point for each separate reward). Do the same for costs. Subtract the two. Do your relationships operate according to the social exchange model? (p. 341)

Relationship	Rewards	Costs	Outcome (Profit)
1.			
2.			

2. Make a list of role expectations of you as a student. Check those which are also role demands. Identify by short statement those which are involved in role conflict. (p. 344)

Role Expectations of You as Student	Role Demands (Check)	Role Conflict (Identify)

3. We often learn by observing the behavior of other people. If it is difficult for you to reach out to others in a male/female relationship, copy someone who seems to know how to make contact. Look for specifics. How does the person begin and end conversations? What type of eye contact does he/she employ? Are the hands used to express feelings, etc.?

Methods Used

To begin a conversation

To end a conversation

Eye contact

Body posture

Use of hands

4. Focus on a fellow classmember you know nothing about. What are your first impressions? After rating the person on the traits, talk to him/her for a few minutes. Would you change some of your opinions? (p. 351)

First Impression	(Check)	Changes (Identify Only)
Likeable	_____	_____
Successful	_____	_____
Healthy	_____	_____
Good physical shape	_____	_____
Efficient	_____	_____
Daydreamer	_____	_____
Sexy	_____	_____
Conflicted	_____	_____
Warm	_____	_____
Cold	_____	_____
Relaxed	_____	_____
Harmony	_____	_____
Good listener	_____	_____
Has good ideas	_____	_____
Carefree	_____	_____
Exciting	_____	_____
Smells pleasantly	_____	_____
Lonely	_____	_____
Flirt	_____	_____

5. Make a drawing of the critical events of your life by placing a dot representing your birth, then draw something which represents sequentially the most significant chapters or events of your life.

Meet someone in class and mutually explain your drawings.

Surveying Your Perspective

"Attitudes toward competitiveness have a great deal of influence over personal behavior and motivation. A survey of the literature shows that competitive behavior has been studied in relation to a number of psychological phenomena, including: information processing (Kelly & Stahelski, 1970), aggressive behavior (Berkowitz, 1962; Epstein & Taylor, 1967), interpersonal relationships (Mehrabian & Ksionzky, 1972), achievement motivation (Lubetkin & Lubetkin, 1971), performance (Clark, 1969), and has been shown to be a critical influence in the determination of value structures and life styles (Rappaport, Bernstein, Hogan, Kane, Plunk, & Sholder, 1972)." (p. 303)

Complete this scale using previous instructions.

Competitiveness-Cooperativeness

1 2 3 4 5   1. People who get in my way end up paying for it.

1 2 3 4 5   2. The best way to get someone to do something is to use force.

1 2 3 4 5   3. It is all right to do something to someone to get even.

1 2 3 4 5   4. I don't trust very many people.

1 2 3 4 5   *5. It is important to treat everyone with kindness.

1 2 3 4 5   6. It doesn't matter who you hurt on the road to success.

1 2 3 4 5   *7. Teamwork is really more important than who wins.

1 2 3 4 5   8. I want to be successful, even if it's at the expense of others.

1 2 3 4 5   9. Do not give anyone a second chance.

1 2 3 4 5   10. I play a game like my life depended on it.

1 2 3 4 5   11. I play harder than my teammates.

1 2 3 4 5   12. All is fair in love and war.

1 2 3 4 5   13. Nice guys finish last.

1 2 3 4 5   14. Losers are inferior.

1 2 3 4 5   15. A group slows me down.

1 2 3 4 5   *16. People need to learn to get along with others as equals.

1 2 3 4 5   17. My way of doing things is best.

1	2	3	4	5	18. Every person for his/her self is the best policy.
1	2	3	4	5	19. I will do anything to win.
1	2	3	4	5	20. Winning is the most important part of the game.
1	2	3	4	5	*21. Our country should try harder to achieve peace among all.
1	2	3	4	5	*22. I like to help others.
1	2	3	4	5	23. Your loss is my gain.
1	2	3	4	5	24. People who overcome all competitors on the road to success are models for all young people to admire.
1	2	3	4	5	25. The more I win the more powerful I feel.
1	2	3	4	5	*26. I like to see the whole class do well on a test.
1	2	3	4	5	*27. I try not to speak unkindly of others.
1	2	3	4	5	*28. I don't like to use pressure to get my way.

The (*) is used to indicate the cooperative items; the weights should be reversed for these items. Divide by number of items. Note your score here: _____. If your score is higher than 3 you are somewhat competitive; if lower, somewhat cooperative.

Reference

Martin, H.J., and Larsen, K.S. (1976). Measurement of competitive-cooperative attitudes. *Psychological Reports, 39,* 303-06.

Exploration

At the end of Chapter 1, you described yourself on an adjective checklist. Here, we will use the same checklist and your earlier answers to cast light on your interpersonal relationships.

A. Think for a moment about someone to whom you are attracted and with whom you have had a close, long-term relationship. This will probably be an intimate friend, lover, or spouse. (It's best to avoid using a parent, brother, or sister for this exercise.) Now look at the following list of adjectives, some of which may apply to the person you have chosen and some of which may not. In the space in front of each adjective, write a number to indicate how well that adjective describes the person you have chosen. Use the following scale:

4—Very true of this person; this adjective describes her/him very well.
3—Somewhat true of this person; he or she usually tends to be this way.
2—Not very true of this person; he or she is seldom this way.
1—Not at all true of this person; this adjective doesn't describe her/him at all.

_____ 1. adventurous	_____ 14. stable	_____ 27. narrow	_____ 40. refined
_____ 2. cooperative	_____ 15. irritable	_____ 28. conscientious	_____ 41. energetic
_____ 3. frivolous	_____ 16. methodical	_____ 29. demanding	_____ 42. irresponsible
_____ 4. high-strung	_____ 17. reserved	_____ 30. good-natured	_____ 43. realistic
_____ 5. well-read	_____ 18. intellectual	_____ 31. confident	_____ 44. critical
_____ 6. shy	_____ 19. emotional	_____ 32. sociable	_____ 45. cultured
_____ 7. calm	_____ 20. agreeable	_____ 33. stubborn	_____ 46. soft-hearted
_____ 8. spiteful	_____ 21. careless	_____ 34. responsible	_____ 47. withdrawn
_____ 9. persevering	_____ 22. unshakable	_____ 35. coarse	_____ 48. orderly
_____ 10. unimaginative	_____ 23. self-revealing	_____ 36. retiring	_____ 49. insecure
_____ 11. undependable	_____ 24. inquiring	_____ 37. considerate	_____ 50. naive
_____ 12. talkative	_____ 25. touchy	_____ 38. unpredictable	
_____ 13. clumsy	_____ 26. quiet	_____ 39. worrying	

B. Now think of someone you know reasonably well but find very unattractive and with whom you have had no close long-term relationship. Describe that person on the following checklist using the same 4-point scale.

_____ 1. adventurous	_____ 9. persevering	_____ 17. reserved	_____ 25. touchy
_____ 2. cooperative	_____ 10. unimaginative	_____ 18. intellectual	_____ 26. quiet
_____ 3. frivolous	_____ 11. undependable	_____ 19. emotional	_____ 27. narrow
_____ 4. high-strung	_____ 12. talkative	_____ 20. agreeable	_____ 28. conscientious
_____ 5. well-read	_____ 13. clumsy	_____ 21. careless	_____ 29. demanding
_____ 6. shy	_____ 14. stable	_____ 22. unshakable	_____ 30. good-natured
_____ 7. calm	_____ 15. irritable	_____ 23. self-revealing	_____ 31. confident
_____ 8. spiteful	_____ 16. methodical	_____ 24. inquiring	_____ 32. sociable

_____ 33. stubborn	_____ 38. unpredictable	_____ 43. realistic	_____ 47. withdrawn
_____ 34. responsible	_____ 39. worrying	_____ 44. critical	_____ 48. orderly
_____ 35. coarse	_____ 40. refined	_____ 45. cultured	_____ 49. insecure
_____ 36. retiring	_____ 41. energetic	_____ 46. soft-hearted	_____ 50. naive
_____ 37. considerate	_____ 42. irresponsible		

C. An important idea in this chapter is that, over the long term, people tend to maintain relationships with others who are in most respects similar to them and to avoid people who are different from them. Using the form on page 4-5, you will now have an opportunity to determine the extent to which this is true of your relationships with the two people you have just finished describing. In the column marked Self, copy the ratings that you gave yourself in Chapter 1 on each of the fifty adjectives. Then, in the column marked Friend, copy the ratings you just gave in (A) above to the person whom you find attractive and with whom you have had a long-term relationship. Finally, in the column marked Non-friend, copy the ratings you gave in (B) above to the person whom you find unattractive and with whom you do not have a close relationship. For the moment, leave blank the two columns headed Diff.

	Self	Friend	Diff	Non-friend	Diff
1. adventurous	_____	_____		_____	
2. cooperative	_____	_____		_____	
3. frivolous	_____	_____		_____	
4. high-strung	_____	_____		_____	
5. well-read	_____	_____		_____	
6. shy	_____	_____		_____	
7. calm	_____	_____		_____	
8. spiteful	_____	_____		_____	
9. persevering	_____	_____		_____	
10. unimaginative	_____	_____		_____	
11. undependable	_____	_____		_____	
12. talkative	_____	_____		_____	
13. clumsy	_____	_____		_____	
14. stable	_____	_____		_____	
15. irritable	_____	_____		_____	

16. methodical   ——   ——   ——

17. reserved   ——   ——   ——

18. intellectual   ——   ——   ——

19. emotional   ——   ——   ——

20. agreeable   ——   ——   ——

21. careless   ——   ——   ——

22. unshakable   ——   ——   ——

23. self-revealing   ——   ——   ——

24. inquiring   ——   ——   ——

25. touchy   ——   ——   ——

26. quiet   ——   ——   ——

27. narrow   ——   ——   ——

28. conscientious   ——   ——   ——

29. demanding   ——   ——   ——

30. good-natured   ——   ——   ——

31. confident   ——   ——   ——

32. sociable   ——   ——   ——

33. stubborn   ——   ——   ——

34. responsible   ——   ——   ——

35. coarse   ——   ——   ——

36. retiring   ——   ——   ——

37. considerate   ——   ——   ——

38. unpredictable   ——   ——   ——

39. worrying   ——   ——   ——

40. refined   ——   ——   ——

41. energetic   ——   ——   ——

42. irresponsible   ——   ——   ——

43. realistic   ——   ——   ——

44. critical   ——   ——   ——

45. cultured   ——   ——   ——

46. soft-hearted   ——   ——   ——

47. withdrawn   ____   ____   ____

48. orderly   ____   ____   ____

49. insecure   ____   ____   ____

50. naive   ____   ____   ____

TOTAL DIFFERENCE SCORES   ____   ____

D. If your relationships with these two people follow the rules discussed in this chapter, it is probable that you are much more similar to the person whom you find attractive than you are to the person whom you find unattractive. In order to test this prediction, for each adjective on the list determine the difference between your own rating and the rating you gave your close friend; enter this number in the first column headed Diff. Do the same for the difference between your own rating and the rating you gave your non-friend; enter this number in the second Diff column. When subtracting ratings, don't worry about mathematical signs: a difference of -2 and a difference of 2 should both be listed simply as a difference of 2. When you have determined all the difference scores, add up each column of Diff scores (ignore any minus signs), and enter the totals in the spaces at the bottom of the list.

E. Did you find that you are more similar to your friend than you are to your non-friend? If so, did you and your friend differ greatly on some adjectives (a difference of two or three points)? List these adjectives in the space below. (You might have your friend fill out the form to see if he or she agrees with your rating of these and other characteristics.)

Can you explain why these substantial personality differences don't threaten your close relationship? Perhaps the differences even improve it. Are they characteristics that you wish your friend didn't have? Record your answers to these questions in the space below.

Are you and your non-friend quite similar regarding other adjectives (a difference of zero or one)? Can you explain why these similarities haven't led to a long-lasting and close friendship between you? Are these perhaps characteristics that you do not like in yourself? Is there some other explanation? Record your thoughts about these questions in the space below.

Love, Marriage, and Intimacy

1. If you were to marry, what would you want from your partner? What would you be willing to give? List these. (p. 383)

Desirable Traits in Partner	Your Contribution

2. Interview (separately) a couple married for at least fifteen years. What makes for a successful marriage? What are the pitfalls to watch out for?

Behavior		Pitfalls	
Husband	Wife	Husband	Wife

3. Read a chapter in a book on marriage published in the fifties and a book on the same topic currently published. What is similar and what has changed in our conception of marriage? (p. 383)

Old Text	New Text

4. Thornton's data indicate that couples with children (on the average) are less happy than those without. Interview a couple with small children and make a list of the joys associated with parenthood, and the stresses. Do they balance out? (p. 398)

Joys of Parenthood	Stresses

5. Draw up a marital contract which you and your partner would sign *before* marriage. The contract should define your particular and specific roles with respect to managing money, jobs, raising children, household duties, etc. Ask an opposite sex friend if he/she would be willing to sign such a contract, and why or why not.

Contract

Living together without marriage is reportedly (by your text) the fastest growing alternative to marriage in the U.S. Among college students the incidences range from 20 percent to 30 percent. This is primarily a result of the replacement of the double standard with a standard of permission with affection. Do you agree with this trend? What are your attitudes on cohabitation?

Complete this section using the instructions of preceding chapters.

Cohabitation

1 2 3 4 5   1. Cohabitation is acceptable if two people really love each other.

1 2 3 4 5   *2. Cohabitation is another example of the moral decline of our society.

1 2 3 4 5   3. I plan to cohabitate before marriage.

1 2 3 4 5   *4. Cohabitation is wrong because it is sex without commitment.

1 2 3 4 5   5. Cohabitation is an acceptable lifestyle.

1 2 3 4 5   *6. To be exposed to cohabitation is a bad experience for children.

1 2 3 4 5   *7. Cohabitation is nothing more than living in sin.

1 2 3 4 5   8. Couples should cohabitate for a little while before they marry.

1 2 3 4 5   *9. Couples should save the novelty of cohabitation for when they are married.

1 2 3 4 5   *10. Cohabitation could damage a couple's individual reputations.

1 2 3 4 5   11. Cohabitation is a valuable simulation of a marital relationship.

1 2 3 4 5   12. Cohabitation helps you to understand the duties and responsibilities of marriage.

1 2 3 4 5   13. Cohabitation leads to a sense of security within the relationship.

1 2 3 4 5   14. Lack of commitment is a positive aspect of cohabitation.

1 2 3 4 5   15. I would cohabitate with the "right" person.

		*16. I would not cohabitate.
1 2 3 4 5		*16. I would not cohabitate.
1 2 3 4 5		17. Cohabitation is wonderful.
1 2 3 4 5		*18. Cohabitation is disgusting and cheap.
1 2 3 4 5		*19. Couples involved in cohabitation are cheated from a real love commitment.
1 2 3 4 5		*20. Cohabitation is sinful.

Reverse weights for starred (*) items. Divide by number of items. Note your score here: _____. If your score is higher than 3 you are positive toward cohabitation; if lower than 3, somewhat negative.

The scale items were selected by item analysis from a pool of seventy-seven statements and differentiated significantly between a group of Christian fundamentalists and a group of cohabitors.

Reference

Larsen, K.S. (1986). *Cohabitation scale.* Oregon State University.

Exploration

Throughout this chapter we have emphasized the importance of being alert for early warning signs of stress and of communicating freely and openly with one's partner about concerns, problems, and dissatisfactions before they become overwhelming. The following scale was designed to provide an index of adjustment in two-person relationships where the people are living together. Make several photocopies of the scale or record your answers on a separate sheet so that your partner can also answer the questions and so that you can use this scale in the future.

A. For each of the thirty-two questions, circle the number that most accurately describes your relationship with your partner.

	Always agree	Almost always agree	Occasionally disagree	Frequently disagree	Almost always disagree	Always disagree
1. Handling family finances	5	4	3	2	1	0
2. Matters of recreation	5	4	3	2	1	0
3. Religious matters	5	4	3	2	1	0

4. Demonstrations of affection	5	4	3	2	1	0
5. Friends	5	4	3	2	1	0
6. Sex relations	5	4	3	2	1	0
7. Conventionality (correct or proper behavior)	5	4	3	2	1	0
8. Philosophy of life	5	4	3	2	1	0
9. Ways of dealing with parents or in-laws	5	4	3	2	1	0
10. Aims, goals, and things believed important	5	4	3	2	1	0
11. Amount of time spent together	5	4	3	2	1	0
12. Making major decisions	5	4	3	2	1	0
13. Household tasks	5	4	3	2	1	0
14. Leisure time interests and activities	5	4	3	2	1	0
15. Career decisions	5	4	3	2	1	0

	All of the time	Most of the time	More often than not	Occasion- ally	Rarely	Never
16. How often do you discuss or have you considered divorce, separation, or terminating your relationship?	0	1	2	3	4	5
17. How often do you or your mate leave the house after a fight?	0	1	2	3	4	5
18. In general, how often do you think that things between you and your partner are going well?	0	1	2	3	4	5
19. Do you confide in your mate?	0	1	2	3	4	5
20. Do you ever regret that you married? (or lived together)	0	1	2	3	4	5
21. How often do you and your partner quarrel?	0	1	2	3	4	5
22. How often do you and your mate "get on each other's nerves"?	0	1	2	3	4	5

	Every day	Almost every day	Occasionally	Rarely	Never
23. Do you kiss your mate?	4	3	2	1	0

	All of them	Most of them	Some of them	Very few of them	None of them
24. Do you and your mate engage in outside interests together?	4	3	2	1	0

How often would you say the following events occur between you and your mate?

	Never	Less than once a month	Once or twice a month	Once or twice a week	Once a day	More often
25. Have a stimulating exchange of ideas	0	1	2	3	4	5
26. Laugh together	0	1	2	3	4	5
27. Calmly discuss something	0	1	2	3	4	5
28. Work together on a project	0	1	2	3	4	5

There are some things about which couples sometimes agree and sometimes disagree. Indicate if either item below caused differences of opinions or were problems in your relationship during the past few weeks. (Check yes or no.)

	Yes	No	
29.	0	1	Being too tired for sex.
30.	0	1	Not showing love.

31. The dots on the following line represent different degrees of happiness in your relationship. The middle point, "happy," represents the degree of happiness of most relationships. Please circle the dot which best describes the degree of happiness, all things considered, of your relationship.

0	1	2	3	4	5	6
•	•	•	•	•	•	•
Extremely unhappy	Fairly unhappy	A little unhappy	Happy	Very happy	Extremely happy	Perfect

32. Which of the following statements best describes how you feel about the future of your relationship?

___5___ I want desperately for my relationship to succeed, and *would go to almost any length* to see that it does.

___4___ I want very much for my relationship to succeed, and *will do all I can* to see that it does.

___3___ I want very much for my relationship to succeed, and *will do my fair share* to see that it does.

___2___ It would be nice if my relationship succeeded, but *I can't do much more than I am doing* now to help it succeed.

_____1_____ It would be nice if it succeeded, but I *refuse to do any more than I am doing* now to keep the relationship going.

_____0_____ My relationship can never succeed, and *there is no more that I can do* to keep the relationship going.

[Source: Spanier, 1976]

B. Spanier (1976) used this questionnaire in a study of more than 300 people, some of whom were married and some of whom were divorced. He found that most married people rated their marriage between 97 and 133 on this scale (the average was 114.8); most of the people who were divorced rated their previous marriage between 47 and 99 (the average was 70.7).

Total your score. How does your score compare to these benchmarks? Are you surprised by the results or are they what you expected?

C. Compare your overall score to that of your partner. How closely do your scores agree?

If your two scores differ substantially, look at the individual questions and try to identify those questions on which your answers differed markedly. Do you see any pattern to your disagreements?

Are there aspects of your relationship on which you and your partner agree completely? If so, what are they?

D. Talk with your partner about the results. Discuss especially those questions on which your answers differed significantly; these are likely to be the areas of your relationship where there is a need for better communication. Then pick one or two areas where you and your partner agree that improvement is needed. What are those areas?

Using your text, and any other sources you can locate, what specifically can you and your partner do to improve your relationship in these areas?

In a few weeks or months, come back to this exercise and evaluate the extent to which you were successful in improving these aspects of your relationship. It might be appropriate to try a new strategy, or you might decide to try to improve some other aspect of the relationship entirely. You may also find it helpful to fill out the questionnaire periodically to give you and your partner an index of the quality of your relationship over time and to identify new areas in which improvement is needed.

Sexual Attitudes and Behavior

Activities

1. Your text reports premarital sexual behavior at 81 percent for females and 95 percent for males. What is the law in your state on premarital sex? Outline the essence of the laws focusing on such aspects as discrepancies in age and consent. Should some laws be modified? Why or why not? (p. 427)

2. Visit with permission (as a group) a women's center and discuss with the counselor the relationship of marital happiness to a good sex life. Summarize the main points.

3. The principal theory of human sexual motivation remains drive theory; that is, drive is dependent on the length of time since the last consummatory response (sex act producing an orgasm). However, an alternative not frequently discussed is appetitional theory; that is, motivation is dependent on the experiential pleasure, frequencies, and varieties of sexual intercourse. Read the following article on appetitional theory and state your views on drive versus appetitional theory. (p. 16) *Reference:* Hardy, K.R. (1964) An appetitional theory of motivation. *Psychological Review, 71,* 1-18.

4. What sexual values are promoted by television? For one night, pick out all comments made in regard to sexual behavior and group these into major categories of statements which belong together.

Listing of Statements	Major Category

Surveying Your Perspective

"The literature on homosexuality has been dominated by research on diagnosis, cause, and cure (Morin, 1977). Morin found, in a comprehensive review of the literature, that only 8 percent of the studies dealt with heterosexual attitudes toward homosexuality. Among these, studies of attitudes in the general population of the United States (Levitt & Klassen, 1974), and mental health professionals (Davison & Wilson, 1973) show that respondents are neither well-informed about nor positive toward homosexuals. Furthermore, MacDonald and Games (1974) demonstrated that negative attitudes toward homosexuals are related to beliefs in double standards for men and women. In addition, Churchill (1967) noted that cultures differ in their treatment of, and attitudes toward, homosexuality.

"In other studies (Dunbar, Brown, & Amoroso, 1973; MacDonald, 1974), a positive relationship between authoritarianism and negative attitudes is reported. Hayes and Oziel (1976) and Ross (1975) have explored the relationship between religiosity and attitudes toward homosexuality. Some studies (Altman, 1971; Thompson & Fishburn, 1977; Weinberg, 1972) suggest that males are more prejudiced against homosexuals (or perhaps more afraid). Actual contact with homosexuals calls into question heterosexual stereotypes (Hoffman, 1968). The relationship between contact and a reduction in prejudice has not yet been conclusively demonstrated; however, some researchers have concluded the contact is target and situation specific (e.g., Webster, 1961)." (pp. 245-46)

Heterosexual attitudes toward homosexuality (HATH) scale uses same instructions as for preceding scales.

1 2 3 4 5 1. I enjoy the company of homosexuals.

1 2 3 4 5 2. It would be beneficial to society to recognize homosexuality as normal.

1 2 3 4 5 3. Homosexuals should not be allowed to work with children.

1 2 3 4 5 4. Homosexuality is immoral.

1 2 3 4 5 5. Homosexuality is a mental disorder.

1 2 3 4 5 6. All homosexual bars should be closed down.

1 2 3 4 5 7. Homosexuals are mistreated in our society.

1 2 3 4 5 8. Homosexuals should be given social equality.

1 2 3 4 5 9. Homosexuals are a viable part of our society.

1 2 3 4 5 10. Homosexuals should have equal opportunity employment.

1 2 3 4 5 11. There is no reason to restrict the places where homosexuals work.

1 2 3 4 5 12. Homosexuals should be free to date whomever they want.

1 2 3 4 5 13. Homosexuality is a sin.

1 2 3 4 5 14. Homosexuals do need psychological treatment.

1 2 3 4 5 15. Homosexuality endangers the institution of the family.

1 2 3 4 5 16. Homosexuals should be accepted completely in our society.

1 2 3 4 5 17. Homosexuals should be barred from the teaching profession.

1 2 3 4 5 18. Those in favor of homosexuality tend to be homosexuals themselves.

1 2 3 4 5 19. There should be no restrictions on homosexuality.

1 2 3 4 5 20. I avoid homosexuals whenever possible.

The items which should be reversed in scoring are the following: 3, 4, 5, 6, 13, 14, 15, 17, 18, and 20. Divide by number of items. Note your score here: _____. If your score is higher than 3 you are somewhat positive toward homosexuality; if less, somewhat negative.

"The results of the three phases of the study confirm a predictable pattern of antihomosexual attitudes rooted in a conservative and punitive outlook. Being male, a business student, frequent church attender, responsive to negative peer attitudes, fundamentalist in religiosity, and authoritarian, reflects a punitive outlook where behavior is measured against religious work ethics and morality. This pattern of punitive conservatism is also supported in other studies of heterosexual attitudes toward homosexuality. For example, MacDonald and Games (1974) found that those respondents with negative attitudes were higher in authoritarianism and viewed sex as primarily for procreative purposes. Levitt and Klassen (1974) noted that antihomosexual heterosexuals tended to be found in rural areas and were rooted in fundamentalist religions. Glassner and Owen (1976) noted more sex-role rigidity among respondents with negative attitudes. Collectively, these results point to a pattern of conservative punitiveness not unlike that found for other minority groups. For example, the above array of variables has also been related to negative attitudes toward aborigines in Australia (Larsen, 1978) and appear to be consistent factors of a more general theory of prejudice. . . .

"Homophobia seems rooted in fundamental insecurities of the negative respondent. If negative attitudes largely serve ego defensive functions (Katz, 1960), then general educational programs will probably be of little utility in inducing more tolerance. A better strategy would be to direct attention to the institutional framework of conservative punitiveness, i.e., the churches and organizations which provide the major normative support." (pp. 255-56)

Reference

Larsen, K.S., Reed, M., and Hoffman, S. (1980) Attitudes of heterosexuals toward homosexuality: A Likert-type scale and construct validity. *The Journal of Sex Research, 16*(3), 245-57.

Exploration

Throughout this chapter I have repeatedly mentioned the central role of personal values and attitudes in decisions about sexual behavior. The questionnaire that follows is designed to measure your attitudes about sexual behavior. Answer each item as carefully and accurately as you can by placing a number in the space to the right of each question using the following scale:

0—Strongly disagree
1—Disagree
2—Neither agree nor disagree
3—Agree
4—Strongly agree

_____ 1. I think there is too much sexual freedom given to adults these days.

_____ 2. I think that the increased sexual freedom seen in the past several years has done much to undermine the American family.

_____ 3. I think that young people have been given too much information about sex.

_____ 4. Sex education should be restricted to the home.

_____ 5. Older people do not need to have sex.

_____ 6. Sex education should be given only when people are ready for marriage.

_____ 7. Premarital sex may be a sign of a decaying social order.

_____ 8. Extramarital sex is never excusable.

_____ 9. I think there is too much sexual freedom given to teenagers these days.

_____ 10. I think there is not enough sexual restraint among young people.

_____ 11. I think people indulge in sex too much.

_____ 12. I think the only proper way to have sex is through intercourse.

_____ 13. I think sex should be reserved for marriage.

_____ 14. Sex should be only for the young.

_____ 15. Too much social approval has been given to homosexuals.

_____ 16. Sex should be devoted to the business of procreation.

_____ 17. People should not masturbate.

_____ 18. Heavy sexual petting should be discouraged.

_____ 19. People should not discuss their sexual affairs or business with others.

_____ 20. Severly handicapped (physically and mentally) people should not have sex.

_____ 21. There should be no laws prohibiting sexual acts between consenting adults.

_____ 22. What two consenting adults do together sexually is their own business.

_____ 23. There is too much sex on television.

_____ 24. Movies today are too sexually explicit.

_____ 25. Pornography should be totally banned from our bookstores.

Source: Hudson, Murphy, & Nurius, 1983, p. 260.

Before you add up your score, go back to items 21 and 22 and change the numbers as follows: if you answered 0, change your answer to 4; if you answered

1, change your answer to 3; if you answered 3, change your answer to 1; and if you answered 4, change your answer to 0. Remember to change your answer to both questions 21 and 22. (You may want to keep your original answer in parentheses so that you remember what your real answers to these two questions were.)

Now you can simply add up your total points on this test, which measures liberal versus conservative orientations toward sexual expression. A score between 0 and 50 indicates a somewhat liberal orientation toward sexual expression; the lower the score, the more liberal your orientation. A score above 50 indicates a somewhat conservative orientation toward sexual expression; the higher the score, the more conservative your orientation. It may interest you to know that a group of graduate students in social work averaged about 25 on this scale, while a group of people with fundamental religious beliefs averaged above 50 (Hudson, Murphy, & Nurius, 1983).

Since this is an attitude scale, high scores are no "better" or "worse" than low scores. However, two people who score quite differently on this short test may have incompatible sexual attitudes that could become a source of stress if their relationship continues. With this in mind, you might suggest that your partner take and score the test, and then compare your scores. If you do this, you will probably find that the test is even more valuable if you agree to discuss together those particular questions on which your answers differed the most.

Finally, if you have recorded your answers in the spaces provided, you will find it very interesting to refer back to this test in the future and compare the answers you gave at that time with the answers you have just given. If you discover significant changes in your sexual attitudes over time, it might be worthwhile to think about the reasons why your attitudes have changed.

CHAPTER THIRTEEN

Work and Leisure

Activities

1. Think of your potential career choice. List the requirements for job preparation, expected salary and benefits, and relative autonomy which describes your ideal job situation. List these below. (pp. 465-71)

Job Expectations

Now interview a person presently working in your field. How does the reality of his or her situation match your job expectations?

Conditions of Person in Occupation

2. We live in a society of unemployment and underemployment. What is your strategy if your first choice for a career should for some reason not come to

fruition? What are your second and third choices and how will you get there? (p. 471)

_____

My Second Choice   My Third Choice

_____

_____

3. Ask a person currently occupied in your chosen occupation if you can observe him/her for one hour doing work typical of his/her daily routine. What are your observations?

_____

Your Observations

_____

4. Think of a leisure activity you have never done but often wanted to do. With a proper preparation now do it. In what way was the activity personally meaningful? Discuss.

_____

Your Observations

_____

5. Devise a plan for leisure during your retirement years. What specifically would you do? How frequently would you do it? Can you start just when you retire or must you incorporate meaningful leisure for most of your life and gradually increase the amount upon retirement? (p. 488)

Leisure Plan for Retirement
_____

Surveying Your Perspective

In our day the majority of both males and females work. Women are moving into new fields traditionally thought to be male, yet are on the average still paid only a fraction of male pay. What are your feelings on women's role in the work force? Complete these survey items using instructions for preceding chapters.

1 2 3 4 5 1. Women with the same experience should be paid exactly the same as men.

1 2 3 4 5 *2. Women are best suited for jobs requiring nurturing, like nursing and teaching.

1 2 3 4 5 3. If she wants I would encourage my daughter to become a welder.

1 2 3 4 5 *4. Our biology suggests different occupations.

1 2 3 4 5 *5. Women should stay home and raise their families.

1 2 3 4 5 *6. Men, as heads of households, should be given preference on a job.

1 2 3 4 5 7. Women are paid less because they are discriminated against.

1 2 3 4 5 *8. For women family is first; work is secondary.

1 2 3 4 5   *9. Women simply do not possess the grit to succeed in the competitive business world.

1 2 3 4 5   10. Apart from physical tasks of strength, women can do as well as men in any occupation.

Reverse weights for items starred (*). Add your score and divide by number of items. Note your score here: _____. If your score is higher than 3, you favor equal treatment of the sexes; if less, you favor traditional sex roles.

Exploration

We have seen that choosing the right job or career is a matter of matching your individual characteristics with characteristics of various jobs and careers. This can appear to be an overwhelming problem, but there is at least one way to reduce it to a more manageable size. In fact, the technique you are about to learn can be used to simplify *any* complex decision.

A. If you could create an *ideal* job or career that would fit you perfectly, what would it be like? List on a sheet of paper all the important characteristics of that "dream" job or career. As you generate your list, it may help you also to imagine the worst possible job or career; this should suggest lots of additional ideas for your list of ideal job or career characteristics. You might also think about real jobs or careers that you find attractive and try to identify what it is about those jobs or careers that makes them interesting to you. Think also about people whom you envy because they have the kinds of jobs or careers you would like, and use that as a source of additional ideas. Or alternatively, think of people whose jobs or careers you would hate, and try to determine what specifically bothers you about those jobs or careers. If you wish, ask other people what they are looking for in a job or career or talk to people you know who are happy in their careers and find out what is especially gratifying to them; these may not be desirable features for your job or career, but they may suggest things you overlooked on your list. Don't try to create this list in one sitting; set it aside and come back to it periodically as you think of new things to add.

B. When your list is complete, select the ten or fifteen characteristics that are *most* important in your ideal job or career. Be sure these are worded in such a way that they would be true of your ideal job or career. Then list those characteristics briefly on the form on page 81 in the column headed Characteristic.

Characteristic	Weight	Ratings of Alternatives								
Weighted Total Score										

C. Now assign a weight to each of the characteristics on the form using the following numbers:

8—Absolutely essential for ideal job or career.
7—Very important for an ideal job or career.
6—Fairly important for an ideal job or career.
5—Desirable for an ideal job or career.

For each of the characteristics on the form, put its weight in the column marked *Weight.* You can assign the same weight to all the characteristics, but you will find this exercise more valuable if you use different weights for at least some of the characteristics on the form.

D. To the right of the column for weights, there is a column for each job or career you wish to evaluate. (You can add more columns or photocopy the table if you run out of room.) Put the name of the job or career at the top of its column and then, in the spaces provided, rate the job or career on each characteristic using the following scale:

2—Very characteristic of this job or career.

1—Somewhat characteristic of this job or career.

−1—Not very characteristic of this job or career.

−2—Not at all characteristic of this job or career.

Note the use of minus signs in the ratings and be sure to include those in your ratings when appropriate. You can, of course, rely simply on your impression of each job or career to make these ratings, but in some cases (as the chapter points out) your impression may not be correct. It might be wiser to ask people who are in that job or career to tell you how they would rate the job or career on this scale. Alternatively, you might look up information in your library or career counseling center and use that information to make your ratings. It is important that your ratings be as accurate as possible, so do not try to rush your information gathering. Take your time and be sure that your data are as accurate as you can make them.

When you have rated a job or career on each characteristic, multiply each rating by its corresponding weight. A rating of 2 on a characteristic weighted 6 results in 12 points; a rating of −1 on a characteristic weighted 7 results in −7 points; and so on. For each job or career, add up all the positive points and subtract all the negative points. Enter the total in the box at the bottom of the column for each job.

E. The total points at the bottom of each column tell you how closely each job or career matches the most important characteristics of your ideal. You will probably be surprised to discover that some jobs or careers that you found attractive do not score as highly as you would have expected; conversely, you probably will discover that you had underestimated the desirability of other jobs or careers. If you want to repeat the process for some of the less important job characteristics on your original list, simply follow steps (B) through (D) but use lower weights (5, 4, 3, etc.) for these characteristics since they are less important than your first list. Then you can add the total scores on these characteristics to the original totals and get a new grand total for each job or career.

F. You may discover that none of the jobs or careers you listed comes very close to your ideal. In this case, the next step would be to search out additional information about jobs and careers that come closer to your ideal.

You can use this procedure to help with other complex decisions you face in the course of your life: which of several job offers to accept, which house best fits your needs, which college you or your children should attend, whether to switch from one career to another, whether to purchase a new business, which of several job applicants to hire, and so on. In each case, identify the characteristics that are important in your decision, weight them, rate the various alternatives on each characteristic, and calculate a total score for each alternative. The advantages of this approach are that it forces you not only to think about what is important to you but also to be sure you are well informed on all the available alternatives. It also reduces the sense of being totally overwhelmed by the complexity of the task and, by breaking it into smaller pieces, makes the decision much more manageable. Thus, it reduces the stress that sometimes comes with making important but complex decisions.

Adjusting to Living in Groups

Activities

1. Attend a group meeting and observe conformity behavior. What statements made by people indicated that they were fearful of being perceived as different; had a low opinion of themselves; felt incompetent, ambiguous, or confused; or responded to group pressure as related to a willingness to accept and support group decisions? (p. 499)

	Fear of Being Different	Low Self-Esteem	Expressed Incompetence	Felt Ambiguous	Felt Pressure
1.					
2.					
3.					
4.					
5.					

2. Listen to the evening news for evidence of nonconformists and their work (for example, whistle-blowers in the armaments industry, people engaged in civil

disobedience for a cause, persons protesting a majority decision). List the ways such people help society as a group "to adapt effectively to changing conditions."

_____

How Nonconformist Helps Group or Society _____

_____

Exploration

The following test is an abbreviated version of a test that is widely used to measure _communication apprehension,_ which is "fear or anxiety associated with either real or anticipated communication with another person or persons" (McCroskey & Beatty, 1986). Indicate in the space provided the degree to which each statement applies to you by marking whether you:

1—Strongly Agree
2—Agree
3—Are Undecided
4—Disagree
5—Strongly Disagree

There are no right or wrong answers. Many of the statements are similar to other statements. Do not be concerned about this. Work quickly, just record your first impression.

_____ 1. I dislike participating in group discussions.

_____ 2. Generally, I am comfortable while participating in a group discussion.

_____ 3. I am tense and nervous while participating in group discussions.

_____ 4. I like to get involved in group discussion.

_____ 5. Engaging in a group discussion with new people makes me feel tense and nervous.

_____ 6. I am calm and relaxed while participating in group discussions.

_____ 7. Generally, I am nervous when I have to participate in a meeting.

_____ 8. Usually I am calm and relaxed while participating in meetings.

_____ 9. I am very calm and relaxed when I am called upon to express an opinion at a meeting.

_____ 10. I am afraid to express myself at meetings.

_____ 11. Communicating at meetings usually makes me uncomfortable.

_____ 12. I am very relaxed when answering questions at a meeting.

_____ 13. I have no fear of giving a speech.

_____ 14. Certain parts of my body feel very tense and rigid while giving a speech.

_____ 15. I feel relaxed while giving a speech.

_____ 16. My thoughts become confused and jumbled when I am giving a speech.

_____ 17. I face the prospect of giving a speech with confidence.

_____ 18. While giving a speech I get so nervous, I forget facts I really know.

To score yourself on this test, you should first understand that the test measures fear or anxiety about communication in three different social settings: in *groups,* in *meetings,* and in *public* (in front of an audience).

To get a score for communication anxiety in *groups,* use the following formula, where I represents the item: $18 + (I2 + I4 + I6) - (I1 + I3 + I5)$. In other words, add up your answers to items (2), (4), and (6) and add 18 to that total. Then add up your answers to items (1), (3), and (5) and subtract that number from the previous total. The lowest possible score is 7; the highest possible score is 30. Put your group score here: _____.

For comparison, the average score obtained by nearly 25,000 college students on this scale is 15.4; a score between 10 and 20 should be considered average. A score above 20 indicates above-average anxiety about communicating in groups; a score below 10 indicates a below-average level of anxiety about communicating in groups.

To determine your communication anxiety score in *meetings,* use the following formula: $18 + (I8 + I9 + I12) - (I7 + I10 + I11)$. Add up your answers to items (8), (9), and (12) and add 18 to that total. Then subtract your answers to items (7), (10), and (11) from that total. Again, your final total score should be between 7 and 30. Put that final meetings score here: _____.

The national sample of college students averaged 16.4 on this scale; any score between 11 and 21 should be considered average.

To determine your degree of communication apprehension in *public* settings (in front of audiences), use this formula: $18 + (I13 + I15 + I17) - (I14 + I16 + I18)$. Add up your answers to items (13), (15), and (17), add 18 to that total, and then subtract your answers to items (14), (16), and (18) from the total. Again your final score should be between 7 and 30. Enter that score here: _____.

On the average, the sample of college students scored 19.3 on this scale; a score between 14 and 24 should be considered average.

The Quest for Values

Activities

1. Examine the six value types advocated by Spranger. Around which have you built the unity of your life? Justify your answer. (p. 529)

Value Types	How Manipulated in Your Life

2. Interview a fellow classmate and seek to identify three instrumental and three terminal values. List them. (p. 530)

Instrumental Values	Terminal Values
1.	1.
2.	2.
3.	3.

3. Your text suggests that the "Golden Rule" is an example of the same values found in major religions. Based on standard works (for example, Bible, Koran) of three different religions, can you find one more example of similarity of values? Can you also find examples of dissimilarity of values? Cite specific references. (p. 534)

Religions	Similarity of Values-Reference	Differences in Values-Reference
1.		
2.		
3.		

4. "The authentic person is an individual who loves a truthful, insightful experience." (p. 539) Think of a person in your life who meets these criteria. In what way does that person lead a life of self-fulfillment and concern for the well-being of others? Draw a character profile where you describe some aspects of an authentic person's life. (p. 539)

Character Profile

5. What kind of world do you want to see in the future? How would it differ from our current world system? What can you do and what will you do to achieve this ideal world of the future? Outline in a paragraph your plan for changing the world. (p. 540)

My Plan for Changing the World

The Personal Value Inquiry

The Personal Value Inquiry consists of a number of statements which are valued more by some persons and less by others. First, read each statement and then rate it according to the following scale. Put your rating on the line next to the statement.

1—Extremely valuable to me
2—Quite valuable to me
3—Somewhat valuable to me
4—Of relatively neutral value to me

5—Somewhat non-valuable to me
6—Quite non-valuable to me
7—Extremely non-valuable to me

_____ 1. a sense of aliveness

_____ 2. being as charitable as possible

_____ 3. living in a secure nation

_____ 4. the hope of being wealthy

_____ 5. creating an object of beauty

_____ 6. establishing and maintaining a marriage and a family

_____ 7. owning my own land

_____ 8. a stable world

_____ 9. a world without nations

_____ 10. accepting circumstances for what they are

_____ 11. having good health

_____ 12. playfulness

_____ 13. feeling like a worthwhile person

_____ 14. maintaining an efficient society

_____ 15. spending my time at parties

_____ 16. thinking ideas and enjoying thoughts

_____ 17. having happy healthy children

_____ 18. continually and actively striving for some end

_____ 19. the state of tranquility

_____ 20. defending the oppressed

_____ 21. accepting the inevitable

_____ 22. having equality among all persons

_____ 23. the joy of experiencing

_____ 24. being of service to others

_____ 25. living a comfortable life

_____ 26. the opportunity to become a celebrity

_____ 27. making a contribution to basic knowledge

_____ 28. being part of a happy family

_____ 29. the opportunity to improve my standard of living

_____ 30. a sense of everything being connected

_____ 31. floating along in a casual and carefree state of existence

_____ 32. moderation in all moods

_____ 33. leading a life of freedom

Second, rank all the statements. Select the two statements which are of greatest value to you and write the numbers of those statements in the first column below. Make a check mark next to those statements to indicate you have ranked them. Then find the four statements which are of greatest value among those left. Record their numbers in the second column. Check them off. Continue to record the number of statements called for in each column until you have ranked all the statements.

			___			
			___			
			___			
		___	___	___		
		___	___	___		
	___	___	___	___	___	
	___	___	___	___	___	
___	___	___	___	___	___	___
___	___	___	___	___	___	___
2	4	6	9	6	4	2
1st	2nd	3rd	4th	5th	6th	7th

Number of values in group

Consciousness is largely a self-awareness of our values. Values serve as guides for our behavior, either in terms of end-goals to our existence or as means-ends for getting there. By going through this exercise, you can assess your value system, for example, what is important and less important in your life. Are you satisfied with your sequence of values? Are there end-goals and means-ends you wish to change for the future?

Reference

Simmons, D. 1981. Oregon State University.

Exploration

If you have not yet ranked the eighteen terminal values on page 531, take time to do that now because this exercise builds on your answers to that questionnaire.

A. In the *Exploration* exercise for Chapter 1, you attempted to answer the question "Where Am I Going?" by describing a number of important lifetime goals

(p. 5–6); you also selected the three goals that are most important in your life (p. 6). Compare those goals to your ranking of terminal values in the *Psychology in Action* exercise on page 531 of the text. What are the points of greatest agreement? What goals or values emerge as important in both exercises? List them in the space below.

Were there any important goals that you listed in the *Exploration* for Chapter 1 that received very low rankings on the list of values on page 531? If so, what were they and what does the discrepancy mean?

Were there any terminal values that you ranked highly on page 531 that did not correspond to any of the lifetime goals you mentioned in the *Exploration* for Chapter 1? If so, what were they and what does the discrepancy mean?

    B. Drawing upon the *Exploration* exercise in Chapter 1, your ranking of values on page 531 of the text, and your answers to section (A)—as well as anything else that you have learned about yourself while reading this book—take as much time as necessary to write down your answer to the following question in the space below: *"What are my most important lifetime goals?"*